Addison-Wesley Mathematics

Reteaching Workbook

▲▼ Addison-Wesley Publishing Company

Menlo Park, California ■ Reading, Massachusetts ■ New York
Don Mills, Ontario ■ Wokingham, England ■ Amsterdam ■ Bonn
Sydney ■ Singapore ■ Tokyo ■ Madrid ■ San Juan

Copyright © by Addison-Wesley Publishing Company, Inc.
The workbook pages in this publication are designed to be used with
appropriate duplicating equipment to reproduce copies for classroom
use. Addison-Wesley Publishing Company grants permission to
classroom teachers to reproduce these pages. Printed in the United
States of America. Published simultaneously in Canada.

ISBN 0-201-27407-8

ABCDEFGHIJK-HC-943210

Todd Wehr
Memorial Library

Table of Contents

Understanding Addition and Subtraction

The actions below help you decide what operations to use.

Addition

To find how many in all:

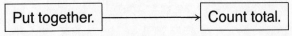

| Put together. | → | Count total. |

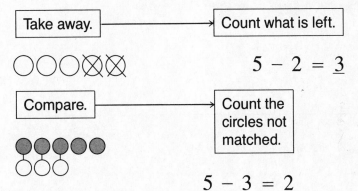

○○○○ ○○   4 + 2 = <u>6</u>

Subtraction

To find how many are left:

| Take away. | → | Count what is left. |

○○○⊗⊗   5 − 2 = <u>3</u>

To find how many fewer:
       (or more)

| Compare. | → | Count the circles not matched. |

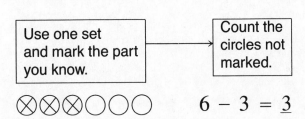

5 − 3 = <u>2</u>

To find the missing part:

| Use one set and mark the part you know. | → | Count the circles not marked. |

⊗⊗⊗○○○   6 − 3 = <u>3</u>

Use counters to find the answer. Complete the equation.

1. 4 children are looking at the bears. 3 join them.

    How many children are there in all?   4 **+** 3 = _____

2. 6 zookeepers are needed to wash an elephant. 2 are there now. How many more are needed?

                              6 **−** 2 = _____

3. You see 8 baby male zebras and 5 female zebras. How many fewer are females?

                              8 **−** 5 = _____

Addison-Wesley | All rights reserved

Addition Properties

Adding Down

$$\left.\begin{array}{r} 3 \\ 2 \end{array}\right\} \text{5 white cars}$$
$$\underline{+\ 2}\quad\text{2 black cars}$$
$$7\quad\text{7 cars in all}$$

Adding Up

$$3\quad\text{3 small cars}$$
$$\left.\begin{array}{r} 2 \\ \underline{+\ 2} \end{array}\right\} \text{4 big cars}$$
$$7\quad\text{7 cars in all}$$

When you add, you get the same sum even when you change the grouping.

Find the sums.

1. $\begin{array}{r}5\\6\\+7\\\hline\end{array}$	**2.** $\begin{array}{r}8\\6\\+2\\\hline\end{array}$	**3.** $\begin{array}{r}9\\1\\+5\\\hline\end{array}$	**4.** $\begin{array}{r}7\\6\\+3\\\hline\end{array}$	**5.** $\begin{array}{r}5\\6\\+5\\\hline\end{array}$	**6.** $\begin{array}{r}1\\2\\+7\\\hline\end{array}$
7. $\begin{array}{r}8\\9\\+2\\\hline\end{array}$	**8.** $\begin{array}{r}6\\1\\+7\\\hline\end{array}$	**9.** $\begin{array}{r}4\\8\\+3\\\hline\end{array}$	**10.** $\begin{array}{r}3\\6\\+9\\\hline\end{array}$	**11.** $\begin{array}{r}8\\5\\+2\\\hline\end{array}$	**12.** $\begin{array}{r}4\\4\\+9\\\hline\end{array}$
13. $\begin{array}{r}5\\4\\+3\\\hline\end{array}$	**14.** $\begin{array}{r}9\\3\\+4\\\hline\end{array}$	**15.** $\begin{array}{r}6\\2\\+7\\\hline\end{array}$	**16.** $\begin{array}{r}5\\3\\+2\\\hline\end{array}$	**17.** $\begin{array}{r}7\\8\\+3\\\hline\end{array}$	**18.** $\begin{array}{r}6\\4\\+2\\\hline\end{array}$

Solve.

19. $6 + 3 + 4 = $ _____   **20.** $5 + 7 + 4 = $ _____   **21.** $8 + 6 + 3 = $ _____

22. $6 + 9 + 4 = $ _____   **23.** $9 + 3 + 5 = $ _____   **24.** $7 + 8 + 2 = $ _____

Name _____

Using Addition to Subtract

| An addition fact shows two addends and one sum. | → | A subtraction fact shows the sum and one addend. | → | You use the sum and one addend to find the other addend. |

$8 + 2 = 10$ $10 - 2 = \boxed{}$ The missing addend is 8.

A fact family shows two addition facts and two subtraction facts for three numbers.

$8 + 2 = 10$ $10 - 2 = \boxed{8}$ $2 + 8 = 10$ $10 - 8 = \boxed{2}$

Add 2 to 8 to make 10.   What number do you add to 2 to make 10?   Add 8 to 2 to make 10.   What number do you add to 8 to make 10?

Subtract. Find the missing addend.

1. $12 - 7 = $ _____   **2.** $11 - 4 = $ _____   **3.** $9 - 3 = $ _____

Give an addition fact for each subtraction fact.

4. $15 - 8 = 7$ **5.** $11 - 1 = 10$ **6.** $14 - 9 = 5$

_____   _____   _____

Subtract.

7. $\begin{array}{r} 12 \\ -\ 8 \\ \hline \end{array}$ **8.** $\begin{array}{r} 15 \\ -\ 1 \\ \hline \end{array}$ **9.** $\begin{array}{r} 14 \\ -\ 7 \\ \hline \end{array}$ **10.** $\begin{array}{r} 9 \\ -2 \\ \hline \end{array}$ **11.** $\begin{array}{r} 10 \\ -\ 4 \\ \hline \end{array}$

Write the fact family for 7, 9, and 16.

12. _____ _____ _____ _____

Addison-Wesley | All Rights Reserved

Name _____

Introduction

Problem Solving Checklist
▶ Understand the situation.
▶ Find data.
▶ Plan the solution.
▶ Estimate the answer.
▶ Solve the problem.
▶ Check.

The checklist can help you solve problems.

Ring the number sentence you could use to solve each problem.

1. Robin picked 15 apples. She ate 6 of them. How many did she have left?

Understand: _How many apples left?_

Data: _apples to start: 15_
apples eaten: 6

Plan: _To find the number left, you subtract._

a. 15 − 6   **b.** 15 + 6

2. John picked 10 bushels of oranges one week. The next week he picked 14 bushels. How many bushels did he pick?

Understand: _____

Data: _____

Plan: _____

a. 10 + 14   **b.** 14 − 10

Solve these problems.

3. Sandy sold 7 bushels of apples one day and 8 bushels the next. How many bushels did she sell?

_____

4. Tom sold 12 bags of potatoes. Larry sold 7 bags. How many more bags did Tom sell?

_____

5. Sally bought 16 ears of yellow corn and 9 ears of white corn. How many fewer ears of white corn did she have?

_____

6. Bill sold 8 squash and Patty sold 6. How many did they sell altogether?

_____

Addison-Wesley | All Rights Reserved

Name _____

Using Critical Thinking

What number am I?

1. I am a 2-digit number between 9 and 19.

2. I am odd.

3. I could not be any less.

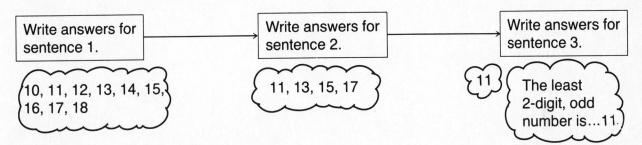

Write answers for sentence 1.	Write answers for sentence 2.	Write answers for sentence 3.
10, 11, 12, 13, 14, 15, 16, 17, 18	11, 13, 15, 17	11 The least 2-digit, odd number is...11.

Solve these secret number riddles.

1. **a.** I am a 3-digit number.
    b. All my digits are the same.
    c. I could not be any greater.

What number am I? _____

2. **a.** I am an even number.
    b. I am between 1 and 10.
    c. I could not be any smaller.

What number am I? _____

3. **a.** I am between 20 and 30.
    b. I am odd.
    c. You say me when you count by fives.

What number am I? _____

4. **a.** I am an odd number.
    b. I am between 10 and 20.
    c. My difference with 8 is less than 4.

What number am I? _____

5. **a.** I am not a 2-digit number.
    b. I am even.
    c. My sum with 9 is between 15 and 20.

What number am I? _____

6. **a.** I am less than 10.
    b. I am a double.
    c. My product with 4 is more than 25.

What number am I? _____

7. Make up a secret number riddle. Give it to a classmate to solve.

Addison-Wesley | All Rights Reserved

Breaking Apart Numbers

12 + 5 = 10 + 2 + 5 ⟩ ▱▱▱▱▱▱▱▱▱▱ + ▱▱▱▱▱

12 equals 10 plus 2 ⟩ ▱▱▱▱▱▱▱▱▱▱ + ▱▱

10 plus 2 plus 5 = 17 ⟩ ▱▱▱▱▱▱▱▱▱▱ + ▱▱ + ▱▱▱▱▱

Use mental math to add.
It may help to break apart an addend.

1. $4 + 9 =$ _____

2. $14 + 3 =$ _____

3. $12 + 4 =$ _____

4. $11 + 6 =$ _____

5. $17 + 2 =$ _____

6. $8 + 6 =$ _____

Use mental math to add.
If you need help, break apart an addend.

7. $\begin{array}{r} 9 \\ + 3 \\ \hline \end{array}$ **8.** $\begin{array}{r} 8 \\ + 9 \\ \hline \end{array}$ **9.** $\begin{array}{r} 4 \\ + 5 \\ \hline \end{array}$ **10.** $\begin{array}{r} 6 \\ + 7 \\ \hline \end{array}$ **11.** $\begin{array}{r} 6 \\ + 5 \\ \hline \end{array}$

12. $\begin{array}{r} 11 \\ + 6 \\ \hline \end{array}$ **13.** $\begin{array}{r} 14 \\ + 5 \\ \hline \end{array}$ **14.** $\begin{array}{r} 12 \\ + 6 \\ \hline \end{array}$ **15.** $\begin{array}{r} 10 \\ + 9 \\ \hline \end{array}$ **16.** $\begin{array}{r} 7 \\ + 8 \\ \hline \end{array}$

Use mental math and the doubles in the table to find
these sums.

17. $27 + 26 =$ _____

$138 + 138 =$	276
$26 + 26 =$	52
$87 + 87 =$	174

18. $86 + 87 =$ _____

19. $138 + 139 =$ _____

Addison-Wesley | All Rights Reserved

Using Compensation

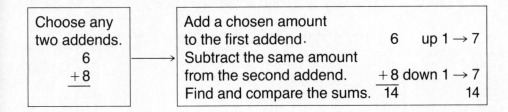

Choose any two addends.	Add a chosen amount to the first addend.	6	up 1 → 7
6 +8	Subtract the same amount from the second addend. Find and compare the sums.	+8 down 1 → 7 14	14

Change to a Double.

Think: 6 + 6 is a double.

4	up 2	6
+ 8	down 2	+ 6
12		12

Change to a Ten.

Think: It is easier to change 12 to 10.

12	down 2	10
+ 7	up 2	+ 9
19		19

Compensate as shown and use mental math to find the sum.

1.
5	down 1
+ 3	up 1

2.
11	down 1
+ 9	up 1

3.
5	up 2
+ 9	down 2

4.
6	up 3
+ 12	down 3

5.
13	down 1
+ 9	up 1

6.
9	up 1
+ 4	down 1

Add. Change to a double.

7.
5
+ 7

8.
9
+ 11

9.
12
+ 8

10.
13
+ 9

11.
16
+ 4

Add. Change to a ten.

12.
11
+ 5

13.
13
+ 5

14.
15
+ 5

15.
8
+ 6

16.
9
+ 6

Understanding Place Value

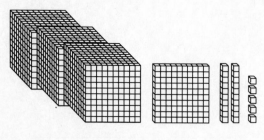

Thousands	Hundreds	Tens	Ones	
3	1	2	5	= 3,125

three thousand, one hundred twenty-five

Write the number for each picture.

1.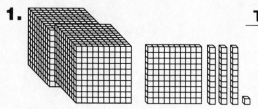

Thousands	Hundreds	Tens	Ones	
2	1	3	1	= _____

2.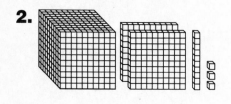

Thousands	Hundreds	Tens	Ones	
				= _____

3.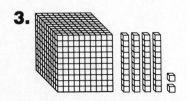

Thousands	Hundreds	Tens	Ones	
				= _____

Write the number in standard form.

4. 7 thousands, 2 hundreds, 6 tens, and 3 ones _____

5. 3 thousands, 7 hundreds, 5 tens, and 1 one _____

6. eight thousand, four hundred sixty-seven _____

7. six thousand, thirty-five _____

8. nine thousand, three hundred two _____

Using Larger Numbers

The thousands period is the next greater period after the
ones. Follow these steps to read a number in the thousands.

▶ Read the digits in the thousands period as a number
   and say the word "thousand" after it.

▶ Then read the digits in the ones period.

Thousands Period			Ones Period		
Hundred Thousands	Ten Thousands	Thousands	Hundreds	Tens	Ones
5	2	4	6	3	7

"five hundred twenty-four thousand"   "six hundred thirty-seven"

You read: "five hundred twenty-four thousand, six hundred thirty-seven."
You write: 524,637.

_____

1. Write a 5-digit number with 4 in
the ten thousands place and 7 in
the thousands place.

2. Write a 6-digit number with 8 in
the hundred thousands place and 4
in the ten thousands place.

___ ___, ___ ___ ___   ___ ___ ___, ___ ___ ___

Write the number.

3. sixteen thousand, four hundred eight _____

4. eighty-seven thousand, one hundred two _____

Ring the correct number.

5. four hundred seventeen thousand, three hundred one

    417,301   417,300   400,017   17,301

6. six hundred twelve thousand, twenty-four

    612,240   612,024   612,000   600,024

Addison-Wesley | All Rights Reserved

Comparing and Ordering Numbers

Which is greater, 5,839 or 5,845?

| To compare these numbers, start at the left. Find the first place where the digits are different. | → | Compare these digits. Which digit is greater? | → | The numbers compare the same way the digits compare. |

same → 5,8**3**9
different → 5,8**4**5

3 4 is greater than 3.
4

5,839
5,**845**

5,845 is greater than 5,839.
5,845 > 5,839

Put these numbers in order, from least to greatest or greatest to least.

5,485   5,839   583   5,893

| To order a list of numbers, compare the numbers two at a time. | → | Then list them from least to greatest or greatest to least. |

583 < 5,839   5,839 < 5,845
5,845 < 5,893

583   5,389   5,845   5,893
5,893   5,845   5,839   583

583 is least.
5,893 is greatest.

Compare. Write < or > for each ◯.

1. 467 ◯ 469   **2.** 4,805 ◯ 4,580   **3.** 54,876 ◯ 543,876

Order these numbers from least to greatest.

4. 546   1,564   678   1,546   **5.** 22,876   786   876   22,799

Order these numbers from greatest to least.

6. 2,876   876   222,876   28,766   **7.** 543   345   2,432   2,345

Addison-Wesley | All Rights Reserved

Name _____

Equality

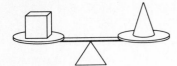

1 cube balances 1 cone.

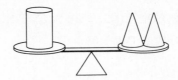

1 cylinder balances 2 cones.

Will this scale balance?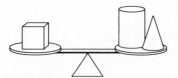

| How many cones balance 1 cube? | → | How many cones are on the right side? | → | Are both sides equal? | YES | The scales balance. |

NO ↓

The scales do not balance.

 balances 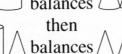 balances, then balances

Some of these scales will balance and some will not. Circle the correct answer.

1.

_____ cones _____ cones

Balance? Yes No

2.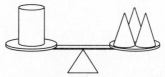

_____ cones _____ cones

Balance? Yes No

3.    Yes No

4.    Yes No

5.    Yes No

6.    Yes No

Addison-Wesley | All Rights Reserved

Name _____

Draw a Picture

To solve some problems, you may find it helpful to draw a picture.

There are four towers.
A is taller than B.
C is shorter than B.
D is shorter than C.
Which tower is the tallest?

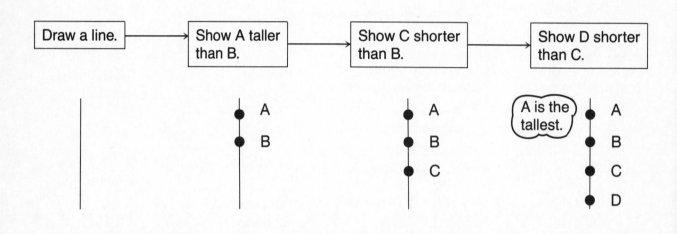

Draw a picture to help you solve each problem.

1. Tower E is taller than Tower F. Tower G is shorter than Tower F. Tower H is taller than Tower E. Which tower is the shortest?

_____

2. Tower J is shorter than Tower K. Tower J is taller than Tower L. The height of Tower M is between Towers J and L. Which tower is the shortest?

_____

3. Tim is shorter than Peter. John is taller than Peter. Roger is shorter than Tim. Who is the tallest?

_____

4. Laurie is older than Ken. Jill is younger than Ken. Chris's age is between Ken's and Jill's. Who is the oldest?

_____

Name _____

Rounding

Rounding to the Nearest Ten

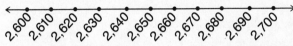

261 through 264   265 through 269
round to 260.   round to 270.

Rounding to the Nearest Hundred

2,601 through 2,649   2,650 through 2,699
round to 2,600   round to 2,700.

Ring the nearest ten for each number.

1. 78 → 70 or (80)

2. 57 → 50 or 60

3. 45 → 40 or 50

4. 234 → 230 or 240

5. 882 → 880 or 890

6. 374 → 370 or 380

Round to the nearest ten. (88 is between 80 and 90. 88 is closer to 90.)

7. 88 → _90_

8. 43 → _____ (43 is between 40 and 50. 43 is closer to 40.)

9. 76 → _____

10. 29 → _____

11. 215 → _____

12. 501 → _____

13. 354 → _____

14. 296 → _____

Ring the nearest hundred for each number.

15. 1,852 → 1,500 or (1,600)

16. 2,341 → 2,300 or 2,400

Ring the nearest dollar.

17. $7.49 → $7.00 or $8.00

18. $59.90 → $59.00 or $60.00

Round to the nearest hundred.

19. 2,184 → _2,200_

20. 632 → _____

21. 3,845 → _____

Round to the nearest dollar.

22. $12.99 → _13.00_

23. $76.15 → _____

24. $45.55 → _____

More About Rounding

Round 4,623 to the nearest thousand.

| Look at the digit to the right of the place to which you will round. | → | Note whether the digit is 5 or more. | → | If the digit is 5 or more, round up. If it is less than 5, round down. |

4,6̸23

To round to the thousands place, look at the digit in the hundreds place.

4,6̸23

6 is more than 5.

4,623 → **5,000**

Round up.

Round each number to the nearest thousand. Ring the digit you will look at. Write the rounded number.

1. 7 ,⌢(3) 4 5 _____7,000_____

2. 1 , 8 0 5 _____

3. 6 , 7 3 4 _____

4. 6 , 3 4 6 _____

5. 1 , 2 5 0 _____

6. 2 , 7 3 1 _____

Ring the nearest thousand for each number.

7. 5,632:   5,000   or ⟨6,000⟩

8. 2,745:   2,000   or   3,000

9. 3,158:   3,000   or   4,000

10. 7,501:   7,000   or   8,000

Ring the numbers in the box that round to 4,000.

11. 4,000 | ⟨4,002⟩   3,403   3,222   4,466   3,892 |

Addison-Wesley | All Rights Reserved

Understanding Millions

The millions period is the third period.
Follow these steps to read a number in the millions.

▶ Read the digits in the millions period as a number
and say the word "million" after it.

▶ Read the digits in the thousands period as a
number and say the word "thousand" after it.

▶ Read the digits in the ones period, if necessary

Millions Period			Thousands Period			Ones Period		
hundred millions	ten millions	millions	hundred thousands	ten thousands	thousands	hundreds	tens	ones
4	1	8 ,	6	3	5 ,	0	0	0

"four hundred eighteen   "six hundred thirty-five
million"   thousand"

You read: "four hundred eighteen million, six hundred thirty-five thousand."
You write: 418,635,000.

---

1. Write an 8-digit number with 5 in
the ten millions place and 3 in the
thousands place.

2. Write a 7-digit number with 4 in
the millions place and 8 in the
hundred thousands place.

__ __ , __ __ __ , __ __ __   __ , __ __ __ , __ __ __

Ring the correct number.

3. thirty-two million, eight hundred five thousand

32,805   (32,805,000)

4. two hundred sixty-three million, two hundred thousand

263,200,000   263,200

5. fifty-eight million, forty-eight thousand

58,048,000   58,048

Counting Change

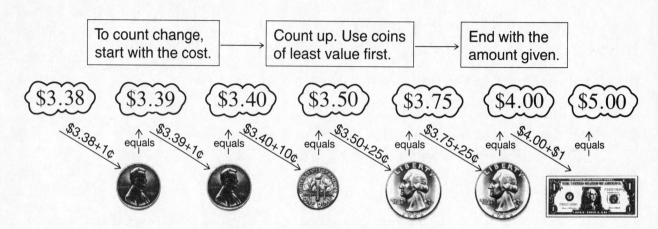

| To count change, start with the cost. | → | Count up. Use coins of least value first. | → | End with the amount given. |

$3.38 $3.39 $3.40 $3.50 $3.75 $4.00 $5.00

$3.38+1¢ equals $3.39+1¢ equals $3.40+10¢ equals $3.50+25¢ equals $3.75+25¢ equals $4.00+$1 equals

Count the change. Write the numbers the clerk would say.

1. You give the clerk $1.00.

84¢

2. You give the clerk $10.00.

$8.50

List the fewest number of bills and coins you could use to pay the exact amount.

3. $16.25

4. $8.49

5. $35.20

6. $18.18

Ring the amount of change.

7. You spend $7.55. You pay $10.00

Your change is: $1.45 $2.45 $3.45

8. You spend $3.98. You pay $5.00.

Your change is: $1.02 $2.02 $3.02

Estimating with Money: Using a Reference Point

Does Ben have enough money to buy a toy dinosaur?

| Find the reference point. | → | See if you can tell at a glance that there is more than enough money. |

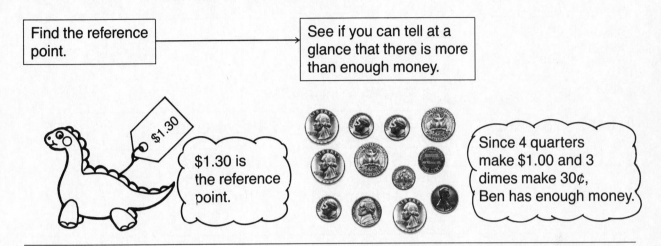

$1.30 is the reference point.

Since 4 quarters make $1.00 and 3 dimes make 30¢, Ben has enough money.

Decide without counting if there is enough money to buy each item. Ring **yes** or **no.**

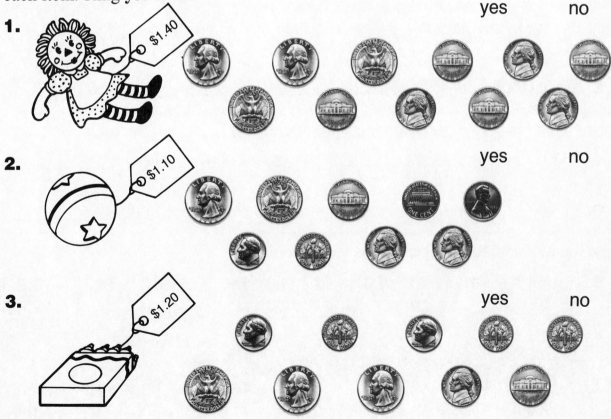

1. yes   no

2. yes   no

3. yes   no

Special Sums and Differences

1 ten = 10 (1 zero)	1 hundred = 100 (2 zeros)	1 thousand = 1,000 (3 zeros)

To Find	Think	Say
70 + 50	7 + 5 tens = 12 tens	120
6,000 + 8,000	6 + 8 thousands = 14 thousands	14,000
1,200 − 300	12 − 3 hundreds = 9 hundreds	900
11,000 − 4,000	11 − 4 thousands = 7 thousands	7,000

Use mental math to fill in the blanks.

1. 60 + 70 = 6 + 7 tens = _____ tens = _____

2. 4,000 + 9,000 = 4 + 9 _____ = _____ thousands = 13,000

3. 600 − 500 = 6 − 5 hundreds = _____ _____ = _____

Use mental math to find these sums and differences.

4. 300 + 500 = _____

5. 3,000 − 2,000 = _____

6. 13,000 + 13,000 = _____

7. 24,000 − 10,000 = _____

Use mental math to find these sums and differences.

8.	**9.**	**10.**	**11.**	**12.**
500 + 400	70 − 20	12,000 − 3,000	8,000 + 2,000	17,000 − 9,000

13.	**14.**	**15.**	**16.**	**17.**
5,000 + 9,000	40 + 30	200 + 600	13,000 − 5,000	8,000 − 5,000

Use with text pages 54-55.

Name _____

Estimating Sums and Differences

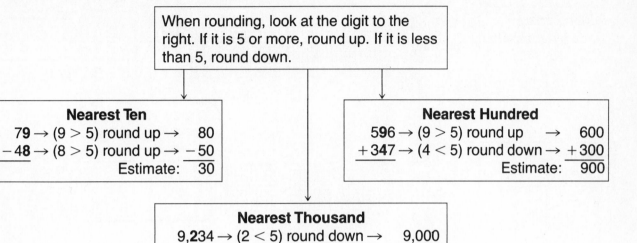

When rounding, look at the digit to the right. If it is 5 or more, round up. If it is less than 5, round down.

Nearest Ten
79 → (9 > 5) round up → 80
− 48 → (8 > 5) round up → − 50
                Estimate: 30

Nearest Hundred
596 → (9 > 5) round up → 600
+ 347 → (4 < 5) round down → + 300
                Estimate: 900

Nearest Thousand
9,234 → (2 < 5) round down → 9,000
− 7,421 → (4 < 5) round down → − 7,000
                Estimate: 2,000

Estimate the sum or difference.
Round to the nearest ten and then add or subtract.

1.   38 →   40
       + 53 → + 50

2.   32
       + 88

3.   81
       − 39

Round to the nearest hundred and then add or subtract.

4.   483 →
       + 209 →

5.   325
       − 225

6.   613
       − 198

Round to the nearest thousand and then add or subtract.

7.   3,682
       + 9,009

8.   8,698
       − 7,598

9.   6,504
       + 7,002

Name _____

Adding Whole Numbers: Making the Connection

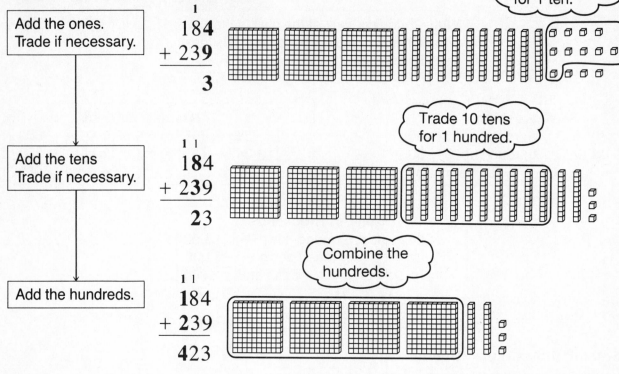

Add the ones. Trace if necessary.

$$
\begin{array}{r}
{}^{1}\\
184\\
+\ 239\\
\hline
3
\end{array}
$$

Trade 10 ones for 1 ten.

Add the tens Trade if necessary.

$$
\begin{array}{r}
{}^{1\ 1}\\
184\\
+\ 239\\
\hline
23
\end{array}
$$

Trade 10 tens for 1 hundred.

Add the hundreds.

$$
\begin{array}{r}
{}^{1\ 1}\\
184\\
+\ 239\\
\hline
423
\end{array}
$$

Combine the hundreds.

Use blocks to find these sums. Record what you did.

1. 758 + 65

2. 467 + 474

3. 683 + 287

$$
\begin{array}{r}
758\\
+65\\
\hline
\end{array}
$$

Use blocks to find these sums.

4.
$$
\begin{array}{r}
{}^{1\ 1}\\
568\\
+\ 284\\
\hline
52
\end{array}
$$
1 + 5 + 2 = 8 Trade? no

5.
$$
\begin{array}{r}
{}^{1}\\
168\\
+\ 540\\
\hline
8
\end{array}
$$
6 + 4 = 10 Trade?

6.
$$
\begin{array}{r}
437\\
+\ 478\\
\hline
\end{array}
$$
7 + 8 = 15 Trade? no

7.
$$
\begin{array}{r}
457\\
+\ 386\\
\hline
\end{array}
$$

8.
$$
\begin{array}{r}
528\\
+\ 396\\
\hline
\end{array}
$$

9.
$$
\begin{array}{r}
403\\
+\ 279\\
\hline
\end{array}
$$

10.
$$
\begin{array}{r}
268\\
+\ 540\\
\hline
\end{array}
$$

11.
$$
\begin{array}{r}
664\\
+\ 258\\
\hline
\end{array}
$$

Adding Whole Numbers

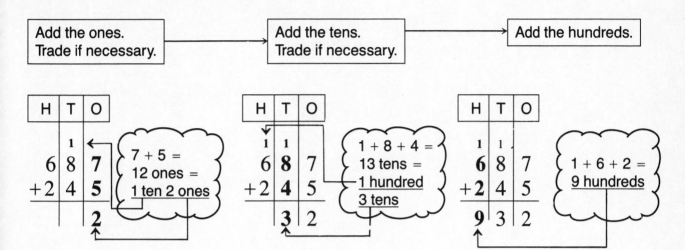

Add the ones. Trade if necessary.	→	Add the tens. Trade if necessary.	→	Add the hundreds.

Find the sums.

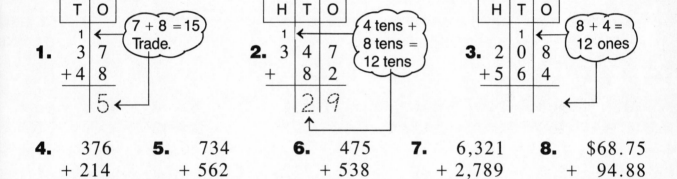

4. 376
+ 214

5. 734
+ 562

6. 475
+ 538

7. 6,321
+ 2,789

8. $68.75
+ 94.88

9. 286
+ 485

10. $42.79
+ 99.54

11. 681
+ 608

12. 926
+ 85

13. 4,627
+ 3,895

Line up the ones digit. Then add.

14. 436 + 872

436
+ 872
------

15. 9,234 + 398

16. $73.00 + $42.85

Name _____

Column Addition

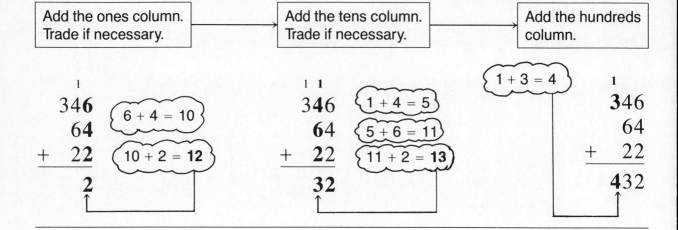

Add the ones column. Trade if necessary.	Add the tens column. Trade if necessary.	Add the hundreds column.

Add.

1. 66	**2.** 54	**3.** 365	**4.** 268	**5.** 222
14	43	297	345	468
+ 56	+ 85	+ 357	+ 463	+ 387

6. 4,365	**7.** $3.76	**8.** 6,532	**9.** $2.66	**10.** 34
262	2.15	78	5.43	776
1,634	6.43	202	0.44	1,345
+ 303	+ 4.09	+ 5,732	+ 4.62	+ 74

11. 32 + 456 + 73 = _____   **12.** $42.78 + $8.29 + $2.34 = _____

13. 472 + 387 + 908 = _____   **14.** 3,405 + 3,026 + 5,408 = _____

Which sum is greater? Ring the answer.

15. 68 + 45 + 32 or 86 + 34 + 12

16. 458 + 82 + 20 or 333 + 88 + 71

Name _____

Make an Organized List

Using the data in a problem to make an organized list may help you solve the problem.

Tom could buy one baseball glove and one bat. One glove was brown, the other was black. He had three colors of bats to choose from—brown, tan, and black. How many choices did he have?

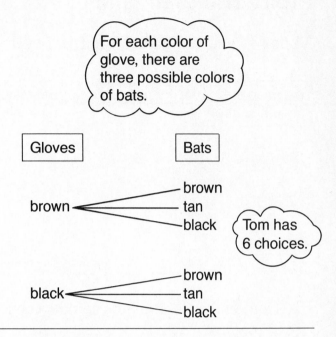

Make an organized list to help you solve each problem.

1. Bill can buy one box of balls and one tennis racquet. The three colors of balls are orange, green, and white. The two types of racquets are wood and metal. How many choices does Bill have?

_____

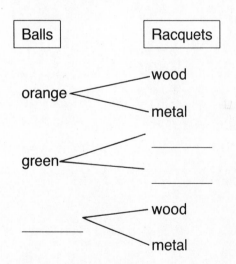

2. The three lengths of fishing poles were 5 feet, 6 feet, and 7 feet. The three styles of reels were bait casting, open faced, and fly. Dick could buy only one fishing pole and one reel. How many choices did Dick have?

_____

3. Kris could buy one sleeping bag and one tent. The two kinds of sleeping bags were box and mummy. The three choices of tents were pup, umbrella, and dome. How many choices did Kris have?

_____

Name _____

Front-End Estimation

To find a close estimation, use **front-end estimation.**

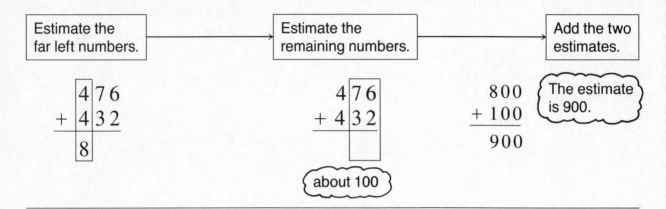

Estimate the far left numbers.	Estimate the remaining numbers.	Add the two estimates.

```
  4|7 6            4|7 6           8 0 0      The estimate
+ 4|3 2          + 4|3 2         + 1 0 0      is 900.
 ___              _____           _____
  8|                |1 0 0|        9 0 0
                  about 100
```

Use front-end estimation to estimate each sum.

1.
```
  3|6 4          3|6 4
+ 2|2 7        + 2|2 7
 ___            _____
  5|            |1 0 0|
              about 100
```

2.
```
  3,|5 8 4        3,|5 8 4
+ 4,|1 2 7      + 4,|1 2 7
 _____           _____
                 about
```

Estimate: _____   Estimate: _____

3. 726
      + 354
      _____

4. $6.38
      + 8.95
      _____

5. 7,832
      + 4,136
      _____

6. 2,136
      + 9,764
      _____

7. 127
        286
      + 865
      _____

8. Is $4 enough for a $2.95 book and a $1.35 magazine?

_____

9. Is $8 enough for a $5.95 game and a $1.35 pad of

paper? _____

10. Which is greater, 495 + 194 or 486 + 139 ?

11. Which is greater, 285 + 521 or 284 + 596 ?

Name _____

Subtracting Whole Numbers: Making the Connection

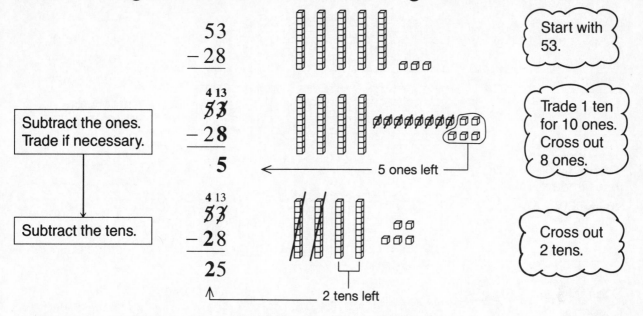

53
− 28

Start with 53.

4 13
5̸3̸
− 28
5

Trade 1 ten for 10 ones. Cross out 8 ones.

← 5 ones left

Subtract the ones. Trade if necessary.

↓

Subtract the tens.

4 13
5̸3̸
− 28
25

Cross out 2 tens.

2 tens left

Use blocks to find these differences. Record what you did.

1. 38 − 19

2. 443 − 181

3. 632 − 327

3̸8̸
− 19

Use blocks to find these differences.

4.
3 15
4̸5̸
− 27
8

Trade 1 ten for 10 ones

5.
6 16
7̸6̸
− 9

Trade 1 ten for 10 ones.

6.
2 12
3̸29
− 87

Trade 1 hundred for 10 tens.

7. 45
− 27

8. 23
− 15

9. 64
− 26

10. 92
− 57

11. 85
− 38

12. 155
− 36

13. 479
− 287

14. 326
− 146

15. 173
− 55

16. 896
− 263

Subtracting Whole Numbers

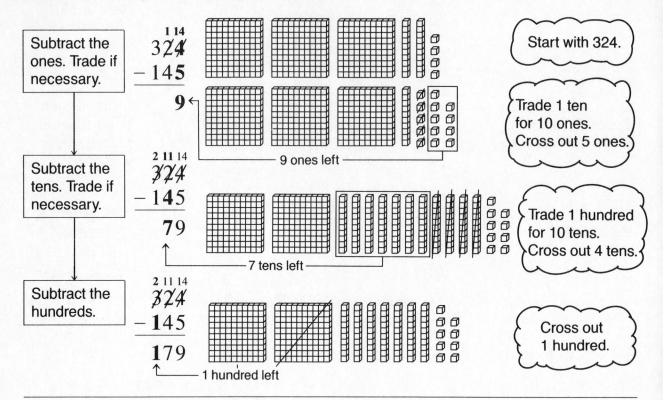

Subtract the ones. Trade if necessary.	$$\begin{array}{r} {\scriptstyle 1\ 14}\\ 3\cancel{2}\cancel{4}\\ -145\\ \hline 9 \end{array}$$	Start with 324.	Trade 1 ten for 10 ones. Cross out 5 ones.
Subtract the tens. Trade if necessary.	$$\begin{array}{r} {\scriptstyle 2\ 11\ 14}\\ \cancel{3}\cancel{2}\cancel{4}\\ -145\\ \hline 79 \end{array}$$	Trade 1 hundred for 10 tens. Cross out 4 tens.	
Subtract the hundreds.	$$\begin{array}{r} {\scriptstyle 2\ 11\ 14}\\ \cancel{3}\cancel{2}\cancel{4}\\ -145\\ \hline 179 \end{array}$$	Cross out 1 hundred.	

Use blocks to find these differences. Record what you did.

1. $583 - 95$

$$\begin{array}{r} {\scriptstyle 4\ \ 17\ \ 13}\\ \cancel{5}\cancel{8}\cancel{3}\\ -\ 95\\ \hline \end{array}$$

2. $678 - 189$

3. $\$3.48 - \$1.59$

Use blocks to find these differences.

4. $$\begin{array}{r} {\scriptstyle 7\ 12\ 15}\\ \cancel{8}\cancel{3}\cancel{5}\\ -276\\ \hline 59 \end{array}$$ Trade tens and hundreds.

5. $$\begin{array}{r} {\scriptstyle 2\ 16\ 15}\\ \cancel{3}\cancel{7}\cancel{5}\\ -\ 87\\ \hline 8 \end{array}$$ Trade 1 hundred for 10 tens.

6. $$\begin{array}{r} {\scriptstyle 6\ \ 12\ 14}\\ \$\cancel{7}.\cancel{3}\cancel{4}\\ -\ 3.68\\ \hline \end{array}$$ Trade.

7. $$\begin{array}{r} 914\\ -456\\ \hline \end{array}$$

8. $$\begin{array}{r} 853\\ -386\\ \hline \end{array}$$

9. $$\begin{array}{r} 772\\ -475\\ \hline \end{array}$$

10. $$\begin{array}{r} 683\\ -\ 94\\ \hline \end{array}$$

11. $$\begin{array}{r} \$5.72\\ -\ 1.86\\ \hline \end{array}$$

Name _____

Subtracting with Middle Zeros

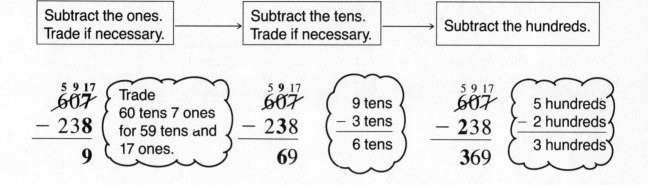

| Subtract the ones. Trade if necessary. | → | Subtract the tens. Trade if necessary. | → | Subtract the hundreds. |

Find the differences.

1.
$$\begin{array}{r} {}^{7\ 9\ 14}\!\!\not{8}\!\not{0}\!\not{4} \\ -\ 176 \\ \hline 28 \end{array}$$
(Trade 80 tens 4 ones for 79 tens 14 ones.)

2.
$$\begin{array}{r} {}^{8\ 10}\!\!\not{9}\!\not{0}9 \\ -\ 68 \\ \hline \end{array}$$
(Do not need to trade ones.)

3.
$$\begin{array}{r} {}^{5\ 9\ 15}\!\!\$\not{6}.\not{0}\!\not{5} \\ -\ 1.47 \\ \hline \end{array}$$
(Trade 60 tens 5 ones for 59 tens 15 ones.)

4.
$$\begin{array}{r} 706 \\ -\ 369 \\ \hline \end{array}$$

5.
$$\begin{array}{r} 503 \\ -\ 219 \\ \hline \end{array}$$

6.
$$\begin{array}{r} 400 \\ -\ 138 \\ \hline \end{array}$$

7.
$$\begin{array}{r} \$9.01 \\ -\ 4.76 \\ \hline \end{array}$$

8.
$$\begin{array}{r} 700 \\ -\ 348 \\ \hline \end{array}$$

9.
$$\begin{array}{r} 503 \\ -\ 259 \\ \hline \end{array}$$

10.
$$\begin{array}{r} 601 \\ -\ 464 \\ \hline \end{array}$$

11.
$$\begin{array}{r} \$8.05 \\ -\ 5.77 \\ \hline \end{array}$$

Line up the ones digits. Then subtract.

12. $505 - 86$

$$\begin{array}{r} 505 \\ -\ 86 \\ \hline \end{array}$$

13. $300 - 185$

14. $\$4.00 - \$2.25$

Using Compensation

Use compensation to find 348 + 202.

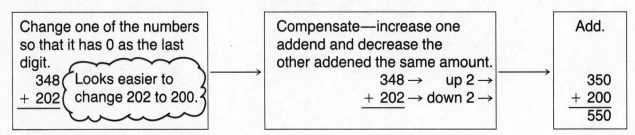

Use compensation to find 468 − 299.

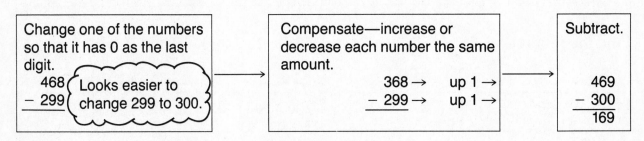

Use compensation to find these sums or differences.
Write the number you used to increase or decrease.

1. 18
   + 42
   ___60 2_

2. 154
   + 46
   ___

3. 125
   − 87
   ___

4. 296
   + 222
   ___

Use compensation to find these sums or differences.
Write the number you used to increase or decrease.

5. 74 + 26 = _____   _____

6. 29 − 14 = _____   _____

7. 21 + 49 = _____   _____

8. 78 − 23 = _____   _____

Use compensation to find these sums or differences.

9. 15 + 45 = _____

10. 86 − 22 = _____

11. 98 + 452 = _____

12. 505 − 82 = _____

Multiple-Step Problems

Sometimes a problem must be solved using more than one operation. These problems are called **multiple-step problems.**

Peter had 124 books in his store. He sold 63 of them on Monday. On Tuesday 12 books were returned. How many books did he have then?

Step 1 Find how many books were left on Monday. <u>Subtract</u> the number sold from the total number of books.

$$124 - \mathbf{63} = 61$$

Step 2 Find how many books there were after 12 were returned. <u>Add</u> the number of books returned.

$$61 + \mathbf{12} = 73$$

There were 73 books.

Solve.

1. Tracy brought $9.25 to the bookstore. She bought two books, one for $3.75 and another for $4.28. How much money did she have left?

Step 1 Add to find the total cost of the books.

$$\$4.28 + \$3.75 = \underline{\hspace{2cm}}$$

Step 2 Subtract to find how much is left.

$$\$9.25 - \underline{\hspace{2cm}} = \underline{\hspace{2cm}}$$

2. Sue ordered 274 books. 118 books came on Thursday, and 120 came on Friday. How many books have not arrived yet?

3. There are 152 books on the shelves. 58 are fiction books, and 64 are nonfiction books. How many other kinds of books are on the shelves?

_____   _____

Addison-Wesley | All Rights Reserved

Name _____

Adding and Subtracting Larger Numbers

Find the sum of 35,466 and 14,967. Find their difference.

Use a Calculator

To Add				To subtract			
Enter	Push	Enter	Push	Enter	Push	Enter	Push
35,466	+	14,967	=	35,466	−	14,967	=

Use Pencil and Paper

Add each place.
Trade when necessary.

$$\begin{array}{r} \overset{1\ 1\quad 1\ 1}{35,466} \\ +\ 14,967 \\ \hline 50,433 \end{array}$$

Subtract each place.
Trade when necessary.

$$\begin{array}{r} \overset{4\quad 13\ 15\ 16}{3\cancel{5},\cancel{4}\cancel{6}\cancel{6}} \\ -\ 14,967 \\ \hline 20,499 \end{array}$$

Add or subtract. Use a calculator or pencil and paper.

1. $\begin{array}{r} 160,743 \\ +\ \ 26,895 \end{array}$ **2.** $\begin{array}{r} 531,922 \\ -\ \ 56,435 \end{array}$ **3.** $\begin{array}{r} 3,768 \\ -1,386 \end{array}$ **4.** $\begin{array}{r} 4,532 \\ +2,487 \end{array}$

5. $\begin{array}{r} 77,468 \\ -12,589 \end{array}$ **6.** $\begin{array}{r} 96,304 \\ -12,659 \end{array}$ **7.** $\begin{array}{r} 17,345 \\ +22,986 \end{array}$ **8.** $\begin{array}{r} 552,667 \\ -324,759 \end{array}$

Use a calculator. Find the number for the ☐.

9. ☐ − 7,965 = 63,498   **10.** ☐ + 12,398 = 76,223

11. ☐ + 43,876 = 124,325   **12.** ☐ − 62,765 = 243,709

13. 625,340 − 347,289 = ☐   **14.** 498,764 + 232,434 = ☐

Deciding When to Estimate

When you solve problems, you can estimate when you need to

▶ compare with a **reference point.**

or

▶ decide **about** how many.

In other situations, you need to find the exact answer.

Alison wants to buy 2 books for $2.95 each. She has $6. Does she have enough money?

> You can estimate because all Alison needs to know is if she has enough money.

Alison bought 2 books for $2.95 each. What amount should she pay the cashier?

> You need an exact answer because she has to pay the correct amount.

Tell if you can estimate the answer or if you need to find an exact answer. Explain why. Then solve the problem.

1. Sally's mom gave her $5 to buy 3 pens for $0.89 each. What amount should she use to tell how much change she needs to return to her mom?

_____

2. Bill bought 2 pads of paper for $1.85 each. What amount should he use to tell a friend about the total cost?

_____

3. Laurie has $25. Is that enough to buy 3 books at $6.95 each?

_____

4. Roger's dad drove 78 miles on Friday and 129 miles on Saturday. What amount should he use to tell a friend how many miles he drove on both days?

_____

Name _____

Getting Information from a Graph

Bar Graph

Pictograph

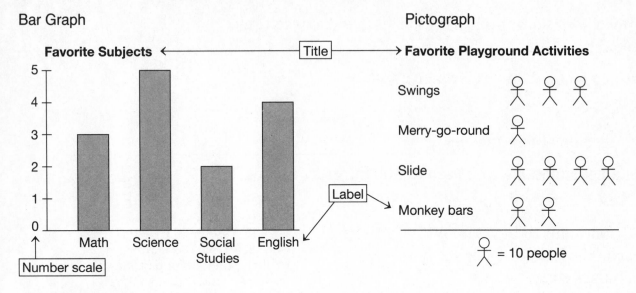

Use the bar graph.

| Look for the correct bar. | → | Follow the bar to the top. | → | Look at the number scale to find out what the bar stands for. |

Use the pictograph.

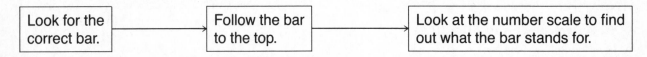

| Find the correct label. | → | Count the number of pictures next to it. | → | Find out what each picture stands for. Add or multiply to get the answer. |

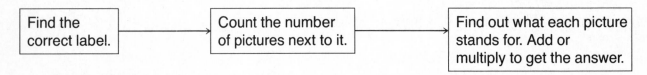

Use the graphs to answer these questions.

1. What is the title of the bar graph? _____

2. What subject was liked the least? _____

3. Which subject was liked more, math or English? _____

4. In the pictograph, what does each ♀ show? _____

5. How many people liked the monkey bars best? _____

6. Do more people like the slide or swings? _____

Reading and Making Bar Graphs

Bob made a bar graph showing how many people wanted to participate in sports in his class.

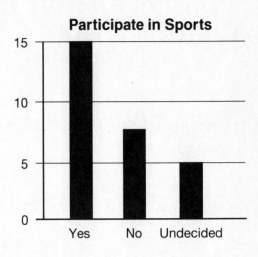

Participate in Sports

How many people said yes to sports?

| Find the Yes bar. | → | Follow the bar to the top. | → | Find the number at the top of the bar. | 15 people |

Sonia made a bar graph to show how many votes for school mascot each animal received.

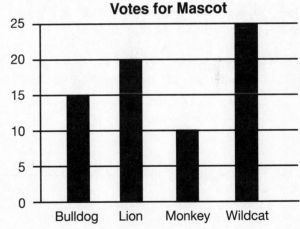

Votes for Mascot

1. How many votes were there for bulldog?

_____

2. How many votes were for lion?

_____

3. How many votes were for monkey?

_____

4. Which animal received the most votes?

_____

5. Which animal received the fewest votes?

_____

Reading and Making Pictographs

This pictograph shows the number of band concert tickets sold by each grade.

Band Concert Tickets Sold

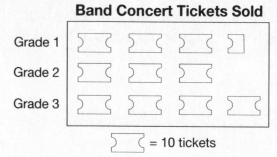

Which grade sold the most tickets? How many did they sell?

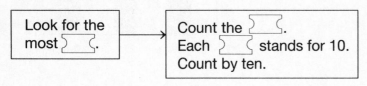

Grade 3 sold the most.
They sold 40 tickets.

Use the pictograph above.

1. Draw the picture symbol used in this graph. _____

2. What does one picture symbol stand for? _____

3. How many tickets did Grade 1 sell? _____

4. How many tickets did Grade 2 sell? _____

5. Make a pictograph to show these data.

**Band Concert Tickets
Sold Each Day**

Monday	15
Tuesday	10
Wednesday	25

Reading and Making Line Graphs

The manager of the Sports Shop made a line graph to show the dollar amount from sales of soccer balls each month for eight months. Use the graph to solve the problems.

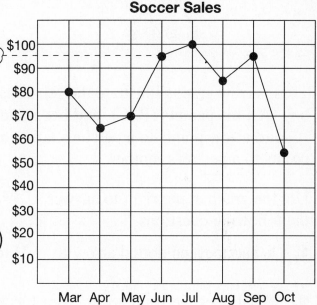

Soccer Sales

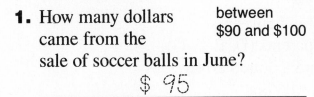

1. How many dollars came from the sale of soccer balls in June? between $90 and $100

$ 95

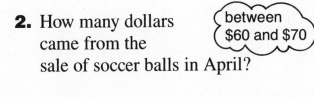

2. How many dollars came from the sale of soccer balls in April? between $60 and $70

_____

3. In what month was the dollar amount from sales of soccer balls the highest?

_____

4. In what month was the dollar amount from sales of soccer balls the lowest?

_____

5. If each soccer ball sold for $5 in May, how many were sold that month?

_____

6. If each soccer ball sold for $10 in March, how many were sold that month?

_____

7. The number of balls sold in November was the same as the number sold in October. If each ball sold for $11, what was the total number of balls sold in October and November?

_____

Addison-Wesley | All Rights Reserved

Using Critical Thinking

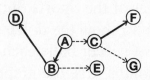

These arrow graphs illustrate the relationship between a boy (A), his parents (B, C), and his grandparents (D, E, F, G). A solid arrow points to a person's father and a dotted arrow points to a person's mother.

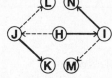

Use the graph at the right to answer the following questions.

1. What does the dotted arrow from H to J show? _____

2. What does the solid arrow from J to K show? _____

3. Is person L male or female? _____

4. What letters represent H's parents? _____

5. What letters represent H's grandparents? _____

Use the graph at right to answer the following questions.

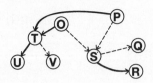

6. Which letters represent the grandparents? _____

7. Which letters represent the parents? _____

8. How many children are there? _____

Which letters represent these children? _____

Name _____

Extra Data

The following problems have more data than you need.
Ring the data that you need and then solve each problem.

1. Ned delivers (75 morning papers) and (58 evening papers). Last week he collected $56 for his paper route. How many papers does he deliver each day?

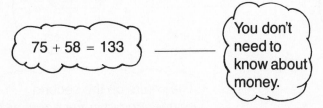

75 + 58 = 133 — You don't need to know about money.

2. Ted is saving money for a new bike that costs $85. He earns $7 a week on his paper route. He has $42 now. How much more money does he

need? _____

3. Pat collected $58 last week and $64 this week. He paid Todd $14. How much more did Pat collect this

week than last week? _____

4. Janet's paper route took her 45 minutes on Monday and 55 minutes on Tuesday. The route is 3 km long. How many more minutes did it take

her on Tuesday? _____

5. A daily paper costs $15 a month. A Sunday paper costs $7 a month. Sally has 42 papers. How much does it cost to buy both papers

each month? _____

6. Peggy had 29 customers on her route. She added 5 new customers last week and 8 new customers this week. How many customers did she

add in the last 2 weeks? _____

7. Mark has 38 homes on his route. He took 30 minutes on Monday to do his route and 27 minutes on Tuesday. How much less time did

he take on Tuesday? _____

8. Sally delivered 48 papers on Saturday, 63 on Sunday, and 52 on Monday. How many more papers did she deliver on Sunday than on

Saturday? _____

Addison-Wesley | All Rights Reserved

Name _____

Fair and Unfair Games

Rules: Spin both spinners.
If the colors match, Team 1 gets a point.
If they do not match, Team 2 gets the point.

Fair Game | Unfair Game

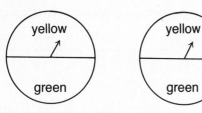

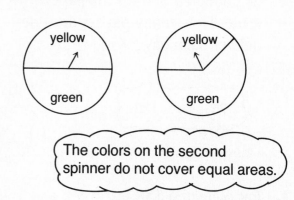

The colors on both spinners cover equal areas.

The colors on the second spinner do not cover equal areas.

The chances of winning are equal.

The chances of winning are not equal.

Play the games below in teams. Cut 2 different colored pieces of paper into 5 strips each, and write a different number (1–10) on each strip. Place strips in a bag. Tell if you think the games are fair. Try to determine why.

1. Color-Match Game
Rules: Each team draws a strip. If the two strips are the same color, Team 1 receives a point. If the colors do not match, Team 2 scores. The first team to get 10 points wins.

2. Sum Game
Rules: Each team in turn draws 2 strips. If the sum of the two numbers is 10 or greater, Team 1 scores. Team 2 scores if the sum is less than 10. The first team to get 10 points wins.

_____

_____

_____

_____

_____

_____

Addison-Wesley | All Rights Reserved

Probability and Prediction

There are 7 marbles in this bag. Which color marble would you have a higher probability of drawing?

| Count the white marbles. | → | Count the black marbles. | → | Decide if there are more black or white marbles. |

You have a **higher probability** of drawing a white marble than a black marble.

___

Which color marble would you have a higher probability of drawing?

1. **2.** **3.** **4.**

_____ _____ _____ _____

5. Predict about how many white paper strips you will get.

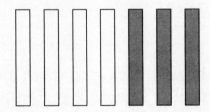

Draw a strip from a bag 30 times. Return the strip after each draw. How did what actually happened compare to your prediction?

_____

6. Predict whether you will get more white or black strips or about the same of white and black.

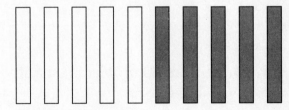

Draw a strip from a bag 20 times. Return the strip after each draw. How did what actually happened compare to your prediction?

_____

Addison-Wesley | All Rights Reserved

Guess and Check

You can use the **Guess and Check** strategy to solve some problems.

Ted has 3 more pencils than Tom.
There are 13 pencils altogether.
How many pencils did Tom have?

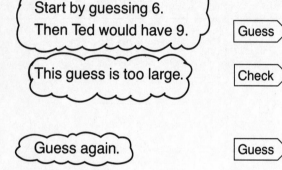

Start by guessing 6.
Then Ted would have 9.

Guess ▷

Tom	Ted
6	6 + 3
	9
6 + 9 = 15	

This guess is too large.

Check ▷

Guess again.

Guess ▷

Tom	Ted
5	5 + 3
	8
5 + 8 = 13	

This checks.

Check ▷

Tom has 5 pencils.

Guess and check to help you solve each problem.

1. Dennis had 11 racquet balls. He had 3 more red balls than blue. How many red balls did he have?

_____

2. Pat sold 14 tapes in two days. There were 2 more sold on the first day than on the second day. How many tapes were sold on the first day?

_____

3. There were 20 problems on Sally's English test. She got 12 more right answers than wrong answers. How many answers did Sally get right?

_____

4. Bob raises ducks and sheep on his farm. The animals in one pasture have a total of 9 heads and 26 feet. How many sheep and how many ducks are there in the pasture? (Remember: sheep have 4 feet, ducks have 2 feet.)

_____

Understanding Multiplication

Juanita has 4 flowers in each garden patch. How many flowers does she have in 3 patches?

$$4 + 4 + 4 = 12$$
$$3 \times 4 = 12$$

When there are the same number of items in each group, you can multiply.

Use counters to find the answer. Then write a multiplication equation that gives the same answer.

1. There are 2 frogs on one pad. How many frogs on 3 pads?

$$3 \times 2 = \underline{\qquad}$$

2. There are 4 socks in each box. How many socks in 2 boxes?

$$\underline{\qquad} \times \underline{\qquad} = \underline{\qquad}$$

3. There are 3 birds in one cage. How many birds in 3 cages?

$$\underline{\qquad} \times \underline{\qquad} = \underline{\qquad}$$

4. There are 5 fingers on one hand. How many fingers on 2 hands?

$$\underline{\qquad} \times \underline{\qquad} = \underline{\qquad}$$

5. There are 9 muffins in each pan. How many muffins in 2 pans?

$$\underline{\qquad} \times \underline{\qquad} = \underline{\qquad}$$

6. There are 7 days in one week. How many days in 2 weeks?

$$\underline{\qquad} \times \underline{\qquad} = \underline{\qquad}$$

Addison-Wesley | All Rights Reserved

Name _____

Multiplication Properties

Order Property	One Property	Zero Property
Changing the order of factors does not change the product.	The product of a number and 1 is that number.	The product of a number and 0 is 0.
$2 \times 4 = 8$ $4 \times 2 = 8$ $2 \times 4 = 4 \times 2$	$1 \times 3 = 3$	$6 \times 0 = 0$

Find each missing number.

1. $3 \times 4 = 12$ **2.** $7 \times 1 = 7$ **3.** $4 \times 0 = 0$ **4.** $3 \times 2 = 6$

$4 \times 3 = $ ___ $1 \times 7 = $ ___   ___ $\times 4 = 0$ $2 \times 3 = $ ___

Find each answer.

5. $2 \times 8 = 16$ **6.** $3 \times 6 = 18$ **7.** $3 \times 5 = 15$ **8.** $6 \times 7 = 42$
$8 \times 2 = n$ $6 \times 3 = n$ $5 \times 3 = n$ $7 \times 6 = n$

$n = $ ___ $n = $ ___ $n = $ ___ $n = $ ___

9. $4 \times 3 = 12$ **10.** $5 \times 2 = 10$ **11.** $6 \times 4 = 24$ **12.** $7 \times 2 = 14$
$3 \times 4 = n$ $2 \times 5 = n$ $4 \times 6 = n$ $2 \times 7 = n$

$n = $ ___ $n = $ ___ $n = $ ___ $n = $ ___

13. $\begin{array}{r} 1 \\ \times 4 \\ \hline \end{array}$ **14.** $\begin{array}{r} 4 \\ \times 0 \\ \hline \end{array}$ **15.** $\begin{array}{r} 3 \\ \times 1 \\ \hline \end{array}$ **16.** $\begin{array}{r} 0 \\ \times 9 \\ \hline \end{array}$ **17.** $\begin{array}{r} 9 \\ \times 1 \\ \hline \end{array}$

18. $\begin{array}{r} 5 \\ \times 1 \\ \hline \end{array}$ **19.** $\begin{array}{r} 0 \\ \times 6 \\ \hline \end{array}$ **20.** $\begin{array}{r} 4 \\ \times 0 \\ \hline \end{array}$ **21.** $\begin{array}{r} 1 \\ \times 8 \\ \hline \end{array}$ **22.** $\begin{array}{r} 2 \\ \times 1 \\ \hline \end{array}$

Factors of 2 and 5

| To find a 2 fact, think about adding doubles. | To find a 5 fact, think about counting nickels. |

  Think: $3 + 3 = 6$.   Think: $5¢ \rightarrow 10¢ \rightarrow 15¢ \rightarrow 20¢$

$2 \times 3 = 6$ $4 \times 5 = 20$

Find each product.

1. $\begin{array}{r} 2 \\ \times 7 \\ \hline \end{array}$ **2.** $\begin{array}{r} 4 \\ \times 5 \\ \hline \end{array}$ **3.** $\begin{array}{r} 6 \\ \times 2 \\ \hline \end{array}$ **4.** $\begin{array}{r} 5 \\ \times 3 \\ \hline \end{array}$ **5.** $\begin{array}{r} 3 \\ \times 2 \\ \hline \end{array}$

6. $\begin{array}{r} 2 \\ \times 9 \\ \hline \end{array}$ **7.** $\begin{array}{r} 6 \\ \times 5 \\ \hline \end{array}$ **8.** $\begin{array}{r} 5 \\ \times 5 \\ \hline \end{array}$ **9.** $\begin{array}{r} 7 \\ \times 5 \\ \hline \end{array}$ **10.** $\begin{array}{r} 2 \\ \times 2 \\ \hline \end{array}$

11. $5 \times 4 = n$ **12.** $7 \times 2 = n$ **13.** $2 \times 9 = n$ **14.** $8 \times 5 = n$

$n = $ _____ $n = $ _____ $n = $ _____ $n = $ _____

15. $2 \times 5 = n$ **16.** $7 \times 2 = n$ **17.** $6 \times 5 = n$ **18.** $5 \times 3 = n$

$n = $ _____ $n = $ _____ $n = $ _____ $n = $ _____

Find the missing numbers.

19. $5 \times \underline{} = 45$ **20.** $8 \times \underline{} = 18$ **21.** $3 \times 5 = 15$

$\boxed{} \times 5 = 14$ $2 \times \boxed{} = 16$ $5 \times \boxed{} = 15$

Find the missing numbers.

22. $4 + 4 = $ _____ $2 \times 4 = $ _____   **23.** $5 + 5 = $ _____ $5 \times 2 = $ _____

A Factor of 9

What is the product of 4 × 9?

| Use 10 product. | → | Subtract the other factor from the product. | → | You will get the same answer using a factor of 9. |

$10 \times 4 = 40$ $40 - 4 = 36$ $9 \times 4 = 36$

Multiply.

 40 – 4   80 – 8   50 – 5

1. $4 \times 9 =$ _____   **2.** $8 \times 9 =$ _____   **3.** $5 \times 9 =$ _____

4. $3 \times 9 =$ _____   **5.** $9 \times 9 =$ _____   **6.** $7 \times 9 =$ _____

7. $9 \times 6 =$ _____   **8.** $9 \times 0 =$ _____   **9.** $9 \times 3 =$ _____

10. $9 \times 4 =$ _____   **11.** $9 \times 8 =$ _____   **12.** $9 \times 2 =$ _____

13.   9
   × 6

14.   0
   × 9

15.   9
   × 9

16.   3
   × 9

17.   9
   × 0

18.   7
   × 9

19.   1
   × 9

20.   4
   × 9

21.   6
   × 9

22.   9
   × 1

23.   5
   × 9

24.   9
   × 5

25.   9
   × 3

26.   8
   × 9

27.   9
   × 2

28.   9
   × 7

29.   2
   × 9

30.   9
   × 8

Factors of 3 and 4

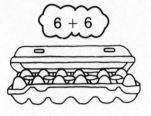

$\boxed{6 + 6}$

$2 \times 6 = \underline{\ 12\ }$

$\boxed{12 + 6}$

2 × 6 plus 6 more

$3 \times 6 = \underline{\ 18\ }$

$\boxed{12 + 12}$

2 × 6 plus 2 × 6

$4 \times 6 = \underline{\ 24\ }$

$\boxed{5 + 5}$

$2 \times 5 = \underline{\hspace{1cm}}$

$\boxed{10 + 5}$

2 × 5 plus 5 more

$3 \times 5 = \underline{\hspace{1cm}}$

$\boxed{10 + 10}$

2 × 5 plus 2 × 5

$4 \times 5 = \underline{\hspace{1cm}}$

Fill in the blanks.

1. $3 \times 4 = 2 \times 4$ plus _____ more = 12.

2. $3 \times 7 = \underline{\hspace{1cm}} \times 7$ plus 7 more = _____.

3. $4 \times 8 = 2 \times 8$ plus $2 \times$ _____ = _____.

4. $4 \times 7 = \underline{\hspace{1cm}} \times 7$ plus $2 \times$ _____ = _____.

Multiply.

5. $4 \times 6 = \underline{\hspace{1cm}}$ **6.** $7 \times 3 = \underline{\hspace{1cm}}$ **7.** $6 \times 3 = \underline{\hspace{1cm}}$

8. $3 \times 9 = \underline{\hspace{1cm}}$ **9.** $4 \times 9 = \underline{\hspace{1cm}}$ **10.** $4 \times 4 = \underline{\hspace{1cm}}$

11. $\begin{array}{r} 3 \\ \times\ 3 \\ \hline \end{array}$ **12.** $\begin{array}{r} 5 \\ \times\ 4 \\ \hline \end{array}$ **13.** $\begin{array}{r} 7 \\ \times\ 3 \\ \hline \end{array}$ **14.** $\begin{array}{r} 8 \\ \times\ 4 \\ \hline \end{array}$ **15.** $\begin{array}{r} 4 \\ \times\ 5 \\ \hline \end{array}$

16. $\begin{array}{r} 9 \\ \times\ 3 \\ \hline \end{array}$ **17.** $\begin{array}{r} 3 \\ \times\ 8 \\ \hline \end{array}$ **18.** $\begin{array}{r} 2 \\ \times\ 4 \\ \hline \end{array}$ **19.** $\begin{array}{r} 4 \\ \times\ 7 \\ \hline \end{array}$ **20.** $\begin{array}{r} 3 \\ \times\ 5 \\ \hline \end{array}$

Exploring Algebra

In these equations, $\triangle$ stands for one number and $\square$ stands for a different number. Find the number that goes in each shape.

| Solve one equation. | $\longrightarrow$ | Solve the second equation. |

$\square \times \square = 4$

$2 \times 2 = 4;$

therefore $\square = 2$.

> Think which equation looks easier to solve.

$\triangle + \square = 11$

$\triangle + 2 = 11;$

therefore $\triangle = 9$.

Find the number that goes in each shape.

1. $\square + \triangle = 7$
   $\triangle \times \triangle = 16$

   $\triangle = \underline{\ 4\ } \quad \square = \underline{\quad}$

2. $\bigcirc + \triangle = 8$
   $\bigcirc \times \bigcirc = 4$

   $\triangle = \underline{\quad} \quad \bigcirc = \underline{\quad}$

3. $\triangle + \triangle = 8$
   $\triangle \times \square = 4$

   $\triangle = \underline{\quad} \quad \square = \underline{\quad}$

4. $\diamond \times \diamond = 25$
   $\diamond \times \square = 30$

   $\diamond = \underline{\quad} \quad \square = \underline{\quad}$

5. $\triangle + 7 = 8$
   $\square - \triangle = \diamond$
   $\diamond + \diamond = 6$

   $\triangle = \underline{\quad} \quad \square = \underline{\quad}$

   $\diamond = \underline{\quad}$

6. $\square + \triangle = \bigcirc$
   $4 \times \triangle = 4$
   $\bigcirc + \bigcirc = 10$

   $\triangle = \underline{\quad} \quad \bigcirc = \underline{\quad}$

   $\square = \underline{\quad}$

7. $\square \times \triangle = 24$
   $\square - \triangle = 2$

   $\square = \underline{\quad} \quad \triangle = \underline{\quad}$

8. $\diamond + \square = \bigcirc + 4$
   $\bigcirc + \diamond = 3$
   $\square \times \diamond = 6$

   $\square = \underline{\quad} \quad \diamond = \underline{\quad}$

   $\bigcirc = \underline{\quad}$

Understanding the Question

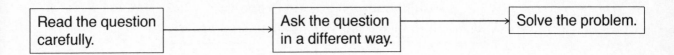

| Read the question carefully. | → | Ask the question in a different way. | → | Solve the problem. |

Ben sold 7 baseballs and 5 basketballs. What is the difference between the number of baseballs he sold and the number of basketballs he sold?

How many more baseballs did Ben sell?

Ben sold 2 more baseballs.

Ring the letter of the question that asks the same thing.

1. Sandy saw 6 robins and 8 bluebirds. How many birds did she see?
  a. How many birds did Sandy see in all?
  b. How many fewer robins than bluebirds did Sandy see?

2. Danny bought 9 goldfish and 7 striped fish. What is the difference in the number of fish?
  a. How many fish did Danny buy in all?
  b. How many more goldfish than striped fish did Danny buy?

Write each question in a different way. Then solve.

3. Cindy planted 8 bean plants and 5 corn plants. How many fewer corn plants than bean plants did Cindy plant?

_____

_____

4. Tom has 2 black cats and 7 gray cats. What is the total number of cats that Tom has?

_____

_____

Addison-Wesley | All Rights Reserved

More Breaking Apart Numbers

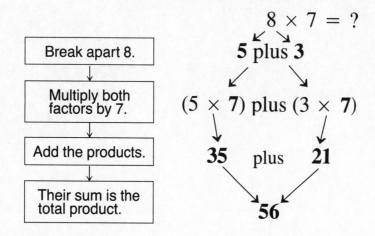

Multiplication-Addition Property
When you multiply, you can break apart a factor.

Break apart 8.

Multiply both factors by 7.

Add the products.

Their sum is the total product.

$8 \times 7 = ?$

5 plus **3**

(5×7) plus (3×7)

35   plus   21

56

Find each product. Show how you break apart one factor.

1. $9 \times 4 = \_\underline{5} \times 4$ plus $\_\underline{4} \times 4 = \_\underline{36}\_$

2. $6 \times 5 = \_\underline{3} \times 5$ plus $\_\underline{3} \times 5 = \_\underline{30}\_$

3. $7 \times 6 = \_\underline{3} \times 6$ plus $\_\underline{4} \times 6 = \_\underline{42}\_$

Find the products.

4. $3 \times 6 = \_\underline{18}\_$ **5.** $5 \times 8 = \_\underline{40}\_$ **6.** $8 \times 4 = \_\underline{32}\_$

7. $7 \times 5 = \_\underline{35}\_$ **8.** $6 \times 6 = \_\underline{36}\_$ **9.** $9 \times 7 = \_\underline{63}\_$

10. $7 \times 1 = \_\underline{7}\_$ **11.** $8 \times 0 = \_\underline{0}\_$ **12.** $4 \times 9 = \_\underline{36}\_$

13. $3 \times 9 = \_\underline{27}\_$ **14.** $4 \times 7 = \_\underline{28}\_$ **15.** $0 \times 5 = \_\underline{0}$

Give the missing number. Then give the product.

16. 5×8 is 40, so

6×8 is $40 + \_\underline{8}$,

which is $\_\underline{48}$

17. 4×7 is 28, so

5×7 is $28 + \_\underline{7}$,

which is $\_\underline{35}$

18. 5×9 is 45, so

6×9 is $45 + \_\underline{9}$

which is $\_\underline{54}$

The Last Six Facts

To find the last six facts,

| Break apart factors. | → | Use the facts you already know. | → | Add the facts. |

$$6 \times 6$$

3   3

$$6 \times 7 \rightarrow 3 \times 7 \text{ plus } 3 \times 7$$
$$6 \times 8 \rightarrow 3 \times 8 \text{ plus } 3 \times 8$$
$$7 \times 7 \rightarrow 5 \times 7 \text{ plus } 2 \times 7$$
$$8 \times 7 \rightarrow 4 \times 7 \text{ plus } 4 \times 7$$
$$8 \times 8 \rightarrow 4 \times 8 \text{ plus } 4 \times 8$$

3×6	18	18	$6 \times 6 = 36$
3×6	18	+ 18	
		36	

Use mental math and the facts you already know.

Find each product.

1. 6
     × 6

2. 8
     × 7

3. 7
     × 8

4. 9
     × 7

5. 5
     × 6

6. 9
     × 6

7. 9
     × 1

8. 7
     × 7

9. 8
     × 9

10. 4
      × 8

11. 5
      × 9

12. 9
      × 7

13. 8
      × 8

14. 7
      × 6

15. 6
      × 9

16. $8 \times 8 =$ _____

17. $9 \times 5 =$ _____

18. $6 \times 7 =$ _____

Which product is greater? Ring the factors.

19. 9×7 or 8×9

20. 5×8 or 6×7

21. 6×7 or 8×6

22. 8×8 or 7×9

23. 9×0 or 8×1

24. 6×9 or 8×7

Multiples

Look for the pattern in the chart.

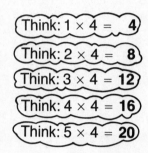

Multiples of 4	
1 × 4	4
2 × 4	8
3 × 4	12
4 × 4	16
5 × 4	20

Think: 1 × 4 = **4**
Think: 2 × 4 = **8**
Think: 3 × 4 = **12**
Think: 4 × 4 = **16**
Think: 5 × 4 = **20**

4, 8, 12, 16, and 20 are **multiples** of 4. You can get these products by multiplying 4 by another number. Continue the pattern to name 3 other multiples of 4. _____

Fill in the charts to find the multiples.

1.

Multiples of 5	
1 × 5	5
2 × 5	
3 × 5	
4 × 5	
5 × 5	

2.

Multiples of 6	
1 × 6	6
× 6	
× 6	
× 6	
× 6	

3.

Multiples of 7	
1 × 7	7
×	
×	
×	
×	

Find the products.

4. $3 \times 4 =$ ____ **5.** $4 \times 5 =$ ____ **6.** $3 \times 6 =$ ____ **7.** $5 \times 7 =$ ____

8. $7 \times 3 =$ ____ **9.** $5 \times 7 =$ ____ **10.** $8 \times 6 =$ ____ **11.** $7 \times 2 =$ ____

12. $\begin{array}{r} 9 \\ \times\ 4 \\ \hline \end{array}$ **13.** $\begin{array}{r} 6 \\ \times\ 6 \\ \hline \end{array}$ **14.** $\begin{array}{r} 3 \\ \times\ 9 \\ \hline \end{array}$ **15.** $\begin{array}{r} 7 \\ \times\ 9 \\ \hline \end{array}$

Make a Table

A **table** can be used to organize data and to help solve some problems.

Fujiko is making play dough. The dough recipe calls for 2 cups of flour and 1 cup of salt. How many cups of salt will she use with 6 cups of flour?

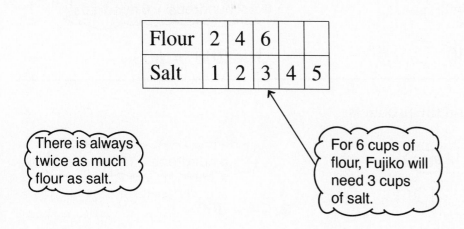

Flour	2	4	6		
Salt	1	2	3	4	5

There is always twice as much flour as salt.

For 6 cups of flour, Fujiko will need 3 cups of salt.

Use the table above to answer Questions 1 and 2.

1. How many cups of flour will Fujiko use with 2 cups of salt?

_____

2. How many cups of flour will Fujiko use with 5 cups of salt?

_____

Jon is going to make mayonnaise. He needs 3 eggs, and 2 cups of oil. Complete the table, then solve these problems.

Eggs	3	6	9		
Oil	2	4	6		

3. Jon needs 8 cups of oil. How many eggs will he need?

_____

4. Jon needs 15 eggs. How many cups of oil will he need?

_____

Special Products

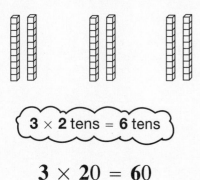

$$3 \times 2 \text{ tens} = 6 \text{ tens}$$

$$3 \times 20 = 60$$

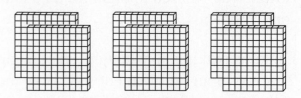

$$3 \times 2 \text{ hundreds} = 6 \text{ hundreds}$$

$$3 \times 200 = 600$$

Use mental math to find the products.

$$4 \times 3 \text{ tens} = 12 \text{ tens}$$ $$4 \times 3 \text{ hundreds} = 12 \text{ hundreds}$$

1. $4 \times 30 =$ _____120_____   **2.** $4 \times 300 =$ _____

3. $4 \times 3,000 =$ _____   **4.** $2 \times 40 =$ _____

5. $2 \times 400 =$ _____   **6.** $2 \times 4,000 =$ _____

7. $3 \times 50 =$ _____   **8.** $3 \times 500 =$ _____

9. $3 \times 5,000 =$ _____   **10.** $4 \times 70 =$ _____

11. $4 \times 700 =$ _____   **12.** $4 \times 7,000 =$ _____

13. $5 \times 80 =$ _____   **14.** $5 \times 800 =$ _____

15. $5 \times 8,000 =$ _____   **16.** $7 \times 10 =$ _____

17. $9 \times 40 =$ _____   **18.** $3 \times 6,000 =$ _____

19. $4 \times 2,000 =$ _____   **20.** $7 \times 600 =$ _____

21. $3 \times 70 =$ _____   **22.** $8 \times 30 =$ _____

Estimating Products

To **estimate** products, you should round and multiply.

| Estimate to the nearest ten. | Estimate to the nearest hundred. | Estimate to the nearest dollar. |

4 x 57   Think: 7 > 5, so round up.

{4 x 60 = 240}

About 240

3 x 429   Think: 2 < 5, so round down.

{3 x 400 = 1,200}

About 1,200

7 x $3.89   Think: 8 > 5, so round up.

{7 x $4 = $28}

About $28

Round to the nearest ten. Then estimate the product.

1. 3×21 _3_ $\times$ _20_ = _60_   **2.** 6×48 _6_ $\times$ _50_ = _____

3. 4×77 _4_ $\times$ _____ = _____   **4.** 7×43 _____ $\times$ _____ = _____

5. 5×78 _____ $\times$ _____ = _____   **6.** 9×32 _____ $\times$ _____ = _____

Round to the nearest hundred. Then estimate the product.

7. 2×732 _2_ $\times$ _700_ = _1,400_   **8.** 6×375 _6_ $\times$ _400_ = _____

9. 5×425 _5_ $\times$ _____ = _____   **10.** 4×679 _____ $\times$ _____ = _____

11. 3×211 _____ $\times$ _____ = _____   **12.** 8×783 _____ $\times$ _____ = _____

Round to the nearest dollar. Then estimate the product.

13. 4 x $8.40 _4_ $\times$ _$8_ = _$32_   **14.** 6 x $3.78 _____ $\times$ _____ = _____

15. 3 x $9.42 _3_ $\times$ _____ = _____   **16.** 5 x $4.15 _____ $\times$ _____ = _____

Multiply and Then Add

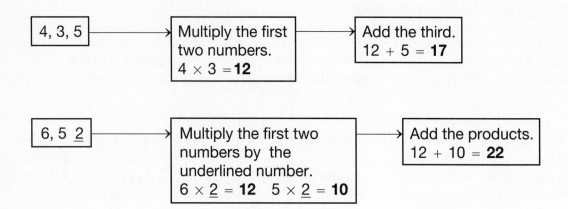

Multiply the first two numbers. Then add the third.

1. 8×2 8   _____   **2.** 5×6 4   _____   **3.** 4×6 7   _____

4. 6×7 3   _____   **5.** 8×9 3   _____   **6.** 7×5 5   _____

7. 3×9 4   _____   **8.** 8×3 6   _____   **9.** 7×7 4   _____

Multiply the first two numbers by the underlined number.
Then add the products.

10. $10, 4$ $\underline{3}$ _____   **11.** $40, 5$ $\underline{5}$ _____   **14.** $12, 3$ $\underline{2}$ _____

13. $50, 1$ $\underline{4}$ _____   **14.** $10, 3$ $\underline{8}$ _____   **15.** $30, 10$ $\underline{3}$ _____

Write the missing number in each ☐.

16. $4 \times 5 + \boxed{} = 21$ **17.** $8 \times 9 + \boxed{} = 74$ **18.** $6 \times 7 + \boxed{} = 49$

19. $4 \times 6 + \boxed{} = 30$ **20.** $6 \times 9 + \boxed{} = 55$ **21.** $8 \times 8 + \boxed{} = 66$

Multiplying Whole Numbers

Use blocks to find 45 x 3.

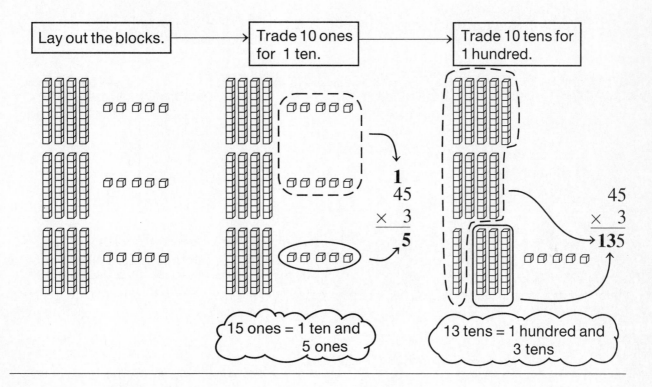

Lay out the blocks. → Trade 10 ones for 1 ten. → Trade 10 tens for 1 hundred.

15 ones = 1 ten and 5 ones

13 tens = 1 hundred and 3 tens

$$\begin{array}{r} 1 \\ 45 \\ \times\ 3 \\ \hline 5 \end{array}$$

$$\begin{array}{r} 45 \\ \times\ 3 \\ \hline \mathbf{135} \end{array}$$

Use blocks to find these products.

1. $14 \times 3 =$ _____

2. $27 \times 4 =$ _____

3. $32 \times 5 =$ _____

4. $25 \times 6 =$ _____

5. $62 \times 5 =$ _____

6. $23 \times 7 =$ _____

7. $26 \times 8 =$ _____

8. $52 \times 5 =$ _____

9. $43 \times 6 =$ _____

10. $55 \times 3 =$ _____

11. $46 \times 5 =$ _____

12. $33 \times 8 =$ _____

Multiplying 2-Digit Numbers

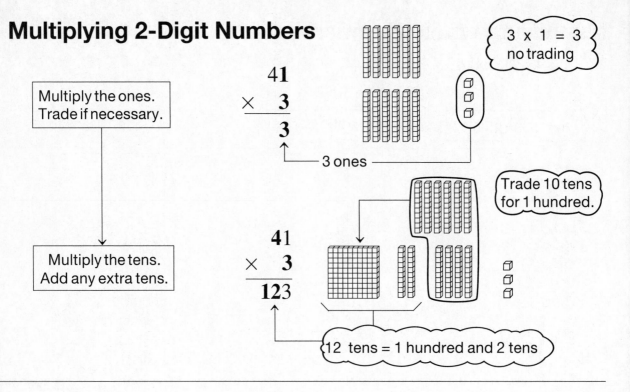

Multiply the ones.
Trade if necessary.

Multiply the tens.
Add any extra tens.

$$\begin{array}{r} 41 \\ \times\ 3 \\ \hline 3 \end{array}$$

3 × 1 = 3
no trading

—— 3 ones ——

$$\begin{array}{r} 41 \\ \times\ 3 \\ \hline 123 \end{array}$$

Trade 10 tens
for 1 hundred.

12 tens = 1 hundred and 2 tens

Find the products.

1.
$$\begin{array}{r} \overset{1}{2}2 \\ \times\ \ 8 \\ \hline 176 \end{array}$$
17 tens is
7 tens and
1 hundred.

2.
$$\begin{array}{r} \overset{1}{3}4 \\ \times\ \ 4 \\ \hline 6 \end{array}$$
13 tens
Trade.

3.
$$\begin{array}{r} 12 \\ \times\ \ 9 \\ \hline \end{array}$$
Trade?

4.
$$\begin{array}{r} 52 \\ \times\ 4 \\ \hline \end{array}$$

5.
$$\begin{array}{r} 43 \\ \times\ 8 \\ \hline \end{array}$$

6.
$$\begin{array}{r} 34 \\ \times\ 2 \\ \hline \end{array}$$

7.
$$\begin{array}{r} 52 \\ \times\ 6 \\ \hline \end{array}$$

8.
$$\begin{array}{r} 38 \\ \times\ 9 \\ \hline \end{array}$$

9.
$$\begin{array}{r} 67 \\ \times\ 5 \\ \hline \end{array}$$

10.
$$\begin{array}{r} 52 \\ \times\ 7 \\ \hline \end{array}$$

11.
$$\begin{array}{r} 28 \\ \times\ 3 \\ \hline \end{array}$$

12.
$$\begin{array}{r} 94 \\ \times\ 5 \\ \hline \end{array}$$

13.
$$\begin{array}{r} 77 \\ \times\ 8 \\ \hline \end{array}$$

Rewrite and then find the products.

14. 6 × 43
$$\begin{array}{r} 43 \\ \times\ 6 \\ \hline \end{array}$$

15. 4 × 86
$$\begin{array}{r} 86 \\ \times\ 4 \\ \hline \end{array}$$

Name _____

Multiplying Larger Numbers: 1 Trade

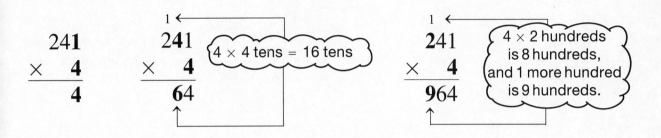

Find the products.

1.   520 3×5 hundreds
      $\times\ \ \ 3$ is 15 hundreds.
      —————   Trade.
        60

2.   161 5×6 tens **3.**   224 $4 \times 4 = 16$
      $\times\ \ \ 5$ is 30 tens. $\times\ \ \ 4$ Trade.
      —————   Trade.   —————
         5

4.   130   **5.**   204   **6.**   422   **7.**   453
      $\times\ \ \ 5$ $\times\ \ \ 3$ $\times\ \ \ 3$ $\times\ \ \ 2$

8.   306   **9.**   171   **10.**   109   **11.**   223
      $\times\ \ \ 2$ $\times\ \ \ 4$ $\times\ \ \ 8$ $\times\ \ \ 3$

Rewrite and then find the products.

12. 4×722 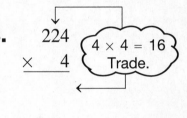   **13.** 3×293 **14.** 6×106

Name _____

Multiplying Larger Numbers: 2 or More Trades

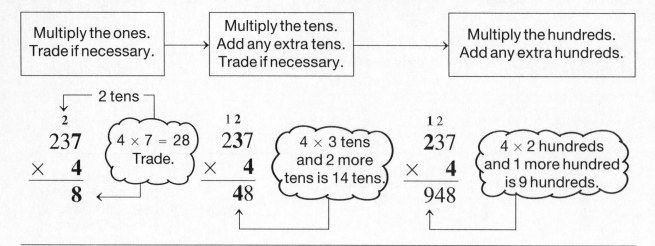

| Multiply the ones. Trade if necessary. | → | Multiply the tens. Add any extra tens. Trade if necessary. | → | Multiply the hundreds. Add any extra hundreds. |

Find the products.

1.
$$\begin{array}{r} {\scriptstyle 1\,2} \\ 249 \\ \times\ \ 3 \\ \hline 47 \end{array}$$
3 × 2 hundreds and 1 more hundred

2.
$$\begin{array}{r} {\scriptstyle 1} \\ 438 \\ \times\ \ 2 \\ \hline 6 \end{array}$$
2 × 3 tens and 1 more ten

3.
$$\begin{array}{r} 678 \\ \times\ \ 4 \\ \hline \end{array}$$
4 × 8 = 32 Trade.

4.
$$\begin{array}{r} 312 \\ \times\ \ 6 \\ \hline \end{array}$$

5.
$$\begin{array}{r} 910 \\ \times\ \ 5 \\ \hline \end{array}$$

6.
$$\begin{array}{r} 401 \\ \times\ \ 8 \\ \hline \end{array}$$

7.
$$\begin{array}{r} 943 \\ \times\ \ 2 \\ \hline \end{array}$$

8.
$$\begin{array}{r} 415 \\ \times\ \ 5 \\ \hline \end{array}$$

9.
$$\begin{array}{r} 823 \\ \times\ \ 7 \\ \hline \end{array}$$

10.
$$\begin{array}{r} 356 \\ \times\ \ 4 \\ \hline \end{array}$$

11.
$$\begin{array}{r} 527 \\ \times\ \ 7 \\ \hline \end{array}$$

12.
$$\begin{array}{r} 568 \\ \times\ \ 6 \\ \hline \end{array}$$

13.
$$\begin{array}{r} 737 \\ \times\ \ 4 \\ \hline \end{array}$$

14.
$$\begin{array}{r} 256 \\ \times\ \ 8 \\ \hline \end{array}$$

15.
$$\begin{array}{r} 673 \\ \times\ \ 3 \\ \hline \end{array}$$

Rewrite and then find the products.

16. 7×650
$$\begin{array}{r} 650 \\ \times\ \ 7 \\ \hline \end{array}$$

17. 5×683

18. 3×178

Name _____

Using Critical Thinking

Bat	24¢
Ball	22¢
Sailboat	16¢
Balloon	5¢

How much will 3 sailboats cost?

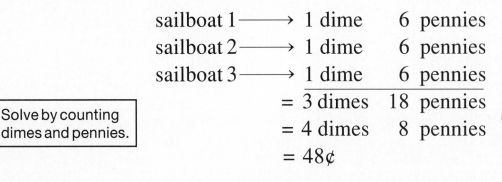

sailboat 1 ⟶ 1 dime   6 pennies
sailboat 2 ⟶ 1 dime   6 pennies
sailboat 3 ⟶ 1 dime   6 pennies
= 3 dimes   18 pennies
= 4 dimes   8 pennies
= 48¢

Trade 10¢ for a dime.

Solve by counting dimes and pennies.

Use a mental math method to find the cost of each of these items.

1. 2 balloons _____

2. 3 bats _____

3. 4 balls _____

4. 2 sailboats _____

5. 3 balls _____

6. 4 bats _____

7. 2 balls _____

8. 3 balloons _____

9. 4 sailboats _____

10. 5 balls _____

11. 2 bats _____

12. 4 balloons _____

Multiplying 3 Factors

> **Grouping Property for Multiplication**
> Changing the grouping of factors does not change the product.

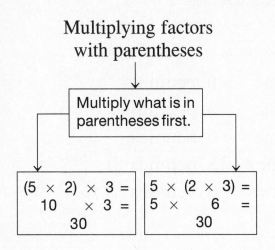

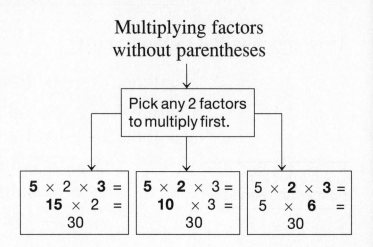

Fill in the blanks.

1. $(2 \times 4) \times 6 =$ _____ $\times 6 =$ _____

2. $7 \times (3 \times 2) =$ _____ $7 \times$ _____ $=$ _____

3. $3 \times (3 \times 3) =$ _____ $\times$ _____ $=$ _____

Use mental math to find the products.

4. $(3 \times 1) \times 9 =$ _____

5. $8 \times (2 \times 3) =$ _____

6. $(3 \times 3) \times 4 =$ _____

7. $4 \times (5 \times 2) =$ _____

8. $6 \times (2 \times 3) =$ _____

9. $7 \times 1 \times 3 =$ _____

10. $50 \times 6 \times 2 =$ _____

11. $4 \times 8 \times 5 =$ _____

12. $10 \times 7 \times 4 =$ _____

13. $6 \times (8 \times 2) =$ _____

Multiplying Larger Numbers: All Trades

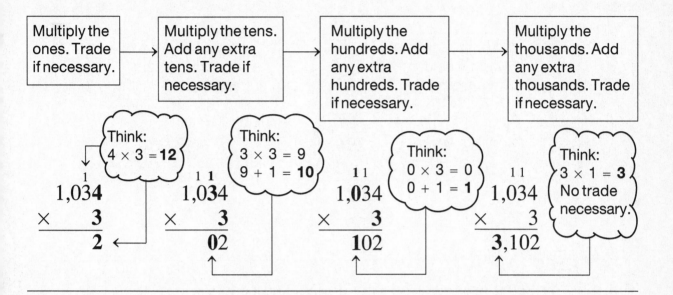

Find the products.

1. 4,328
       × 4

2. 3,515
       × 2

3. 2,034
       × 6

4. 2,032
       × 7

5. 4,824
       × 5

6. 7,412
       × 3

7. 8,120
       × 8

8. 6,008
       × 9

9. 4,022
       × 6

10. 2,001
        × 9

11. 8,024
        × 3

12. 3,505
        × 5

13. $4 \times 5{,}602 =$ _____

14. $1{,}803 \times 5 =$ _____

15. $1{,}530 \times 3 =$ _____

16. $6{,}843 \times 7 =$ _____

17. $7 \times 1{,}001 =$ _____

18. $8 \times 2{,}012 =$ _____

Multiplying with Money

$2.96 \times 7 = ?$

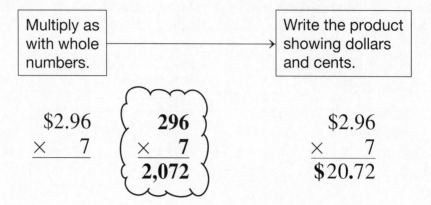

| Multiply as with whole numbers. | → | Write the product showing dollars and cents. |

$\begin{array}{r} \$2.96 \\ \times\quad 7 \\ \hline \end{array}$

$\begin{array}{r} 296 \\ \times\quad 7 \\ \hline 2{,}072 \end{array}$

$\begin{array}{r} \$2.96 \\ \times\quad 7 \\ \hline \$20.72 \end{array}$

Multiply. Write the products showing dollars and cents.

1. $\begin{array}{r} \$5.23 \\ \times\quad 3 \\ \hline \end{array}$
2. $\begin{array}{r} \$4.32 \\ \times\quad 2 \\ \hline \end{array}$
3. $\begin{array}{r} \$0.84 \\ \times\quad 5 \\ \hline \end{array}$
4. $\begin{array}{r} \$6.48 \\ \times\quad 4 \\ \hline \end{array}$
5. $\begin{array}{r} \$2.83 \\ \times\quad 6 \\ \hline \end{array}$

6. $\begin{array}{r} \$12.30 \\ \times\quad 2 \\ \hline \end{array}$
7. $\begin{array}{r} \$14.71 \\ \times\quad 5 \\ \hline \end{array}$
8. $\begin{array}{r} \$10.32 \\ \times\quad 9 \\ \hline \end{array}$
9. $\begin{array}{r} \$0.78 \\ \times\quad 7 \\ \hline \end{array}$
10. $\begin{array}{r} \$11.95 \\ \times\quad 8 \\ \hline \end{array}$

11. $4 \times \$3.26 =$ _____

12. $8 \times \$2.94 =$ _____

13. $9 \times \$5.06 =$ _____

14. $6 \times \$4.86 =$ _____

15. $5 \times \$1.75 =$ _____

16. $7 \times \$1.38 =$ _____

17. $8 \times \$1.78 =$ _____

18. $4 \times \$7.54 =$ _____

Look for a Pattern

Peter put 2 beads in the first bag, 4 beads in the
second bag, 6 beads in the third bag, and so on.
How many beads will Peter put in the sixth bag?

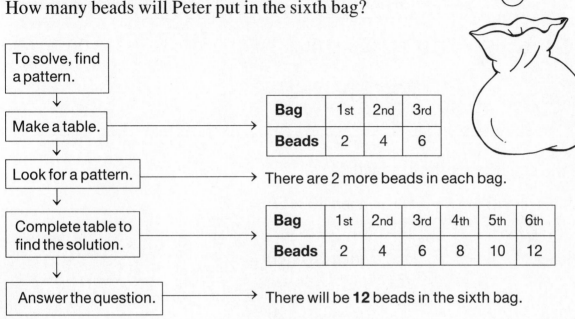

To solve, find a pattern.	

Make a table.	→	**Bag**	1st	2nd	3rd
		Beads	2	4	6

Look for a pattern.	→ There are 2 more beads in each bag.

Complete table to find the solution.	→	**Bag**	1st	2nd	3rd	4th	5th	6th
		Beads	2	4	6	8	10	12

Answer the question.	→ There will be **12** beads in the sixth bag.

Make a table to help solve each problem.

1. Laurie planted 3 bulbs the first
day, 9 bulbs the second day, 15
bulbs the third day, and so on.
How many bulbs will she plant on
the fifth day?

2. Ken mailed 4 boxes on the first
day, 9 boxes on the second day, 14
boxes on the third day, and so on.
How many boxes did he mail on
the seventh day?

3. Jill's mom rode her bicycle 1 mile
the first week, 3 miles the second
week, 5 miles the third week, and
so on. How many miles did she
ride the sixth week?

4. Scott did 5 push-ups the first week,
8 push-ups the second week, 11
push-ups the third week, and so on.
How many push-ups did he do the
seventh week?

Name _____

Special Products

What is the product of 30 × 20?

| Find 3 × 2. | → | Find 10 × 10. | → | Then multiply the two products. |

$3 \times 2 = 6$ $\qquad$ $10 \times 10 = 100$ $\qquad$ $6 \times 100 = 600$

 $\qquad$ $\overparen{30 \times 20}$

Write the numbers for the ☐ and △ .

1. Since $4 \times 2 = $ ☐ , then $40 \times 20 = $ △ .

2. Since $7 \times 6 = $ ☐ , then $70 \times 60 = $ △ .

3. Since $9 \times 2 = $ ☐ , then $90 \times 20 = $ △ .

4. Since $8 \times 3 = $ ☐ , then $80 \times 30 = $ △ .

Use mental math to find the products.

5. $30 \times 40 = $ _____ $\qquad$ **6.** $70 \times 20 = $ _____ $\qquad$ **7.** $90 \times 40 = $ _____

8. $60 \times 50 = $ _____ $\qquad$ **9.** $50 \times 30 = $ _____ $\qquad$ **10.** $80 \times 80 = $ _____

11. $20 \times 70 = $ _____ $\qquad$ **12.** $30 \times 60 = $ _____ $\qquad$ **13.** $70 \times 80 = $ _____

14. $60 \times 60 = $ _____ $\qquad$ **15.** $80 \times 30 = $ _____ $\qquad$ **16.** $90 \times 80 = $ _____

Multiply.

17. $40 \times 90 = $ _____ $\qquad$ **18.** $90 \times 30 = $ _____ $\qquad$ **19.** $80 \times 50 = $ _____

20. $70 \times 90 = $ _____ $\qquad$ **21.** $80 \times 30 = $ _____ $\qquad$ **22.** $70 \times 50 = $ _____

Estimating Larger Products

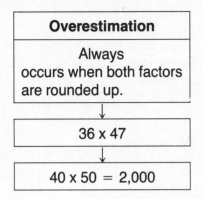

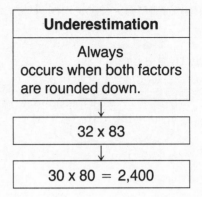

Round to the highest place of each factor to estimate
the product. Circle <u>underestimate</u>, <u>overestimate</u>,
or <u>cannot tell</u>.

1. 23 x 18 _____ underestimate overestimate cannot tell

2. 65 x 38 _____ underestimate overestimate cannot tell

3. 93 x 75 _____ underestimate overestimate cannot tell

4. 475 x 25 _____ underestimate overestimate cannot tell

5. 19 x 191 _____ underestimate overestimate cannot tell

6. 63 x 84 _____ underestimate overestimate cannot tell

7. 72 x $2.18 _____ underestimate overestimate cannot tell

Your reference point is 28,000. Estimate to tell if these
products will be <u>over</u> or <u>under</u> the reference point.

8. 733 x 44   **9.** 698 x 37   **10.** 549 x 62

_____   _____   _____

Multiplying by Multiples of 10

To multiply by multiples of 10,

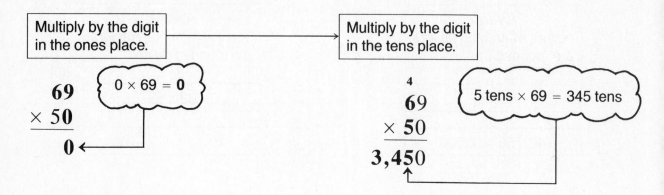

Find the products.

1. 73
     × 10
     ____

2. 63
     × 30
     ____

3. 54
     × 80
     ____

4. 86
     × 90
     ____

5. 39
     × 70
     ____

6. 39
     × 40
     ____

7. 47
     × 20
     ____

8. 26
     × 60
     ____

9. 95
     × 30
     ____

10. 84
      × 50
      ____

11. $56 \times 70 =$ _____

12. $32 \times 80 =$ _____

13. $52 \times 20 =$ _____

14. $49 \times 80 =$ _____

15. $84 \times 30 =$ _____

16. $75 \times 60 =$ _____

17. $26 \times 40 =$ _____

18. $93 \times 20 =$ _____

19. $62 \times 60 =$ _____

20. $99 \times 90 =$ _____

Multiplying with 2-Digit Factors

To multiply with 2-digit factors

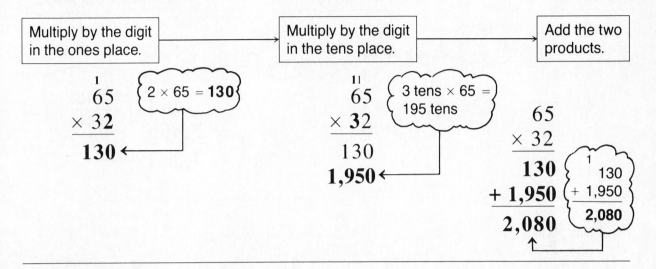

| Multiply by the digit in the ones place. | Multiply by the digit in the tens place. | Add the two products. |

Find the products.

1. 21
  × 23

2. 19
  × 35

3. 41
  × 52

4. 32
  × 24

5. 68
  × 22

6. 94
  × 35

7. 86
  × 98

8. 99
  × 87

9. 47 × 55 = _____

10. 98 × 43 = _____

11. 84 × 23 = _____

12. 75 × 31 = _____

Multiplying with 2- and 3-Digit Factors

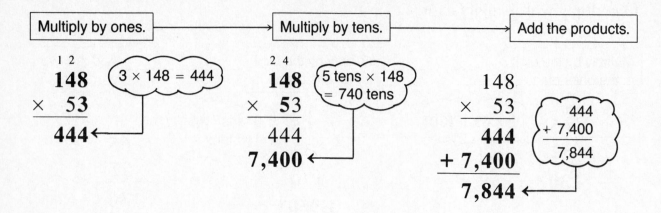

| Multiply by ones. | → | Multiply by tens. | → | Add the products. |

¹ ²
148   3 × 148 = 444
× 53
444 ←

² ⁴
148   5 tens × 148
× 53   = 740 tens
444
7,400 ←

148
× 53   444
444   + 7,400
+ 7,400   7,844
7,844 ←

Find the products.

1. 423
× 45

2. 834
× 68

3. 924
× 26

4. 783
× 79

5. 752
× 25

6. 634
× 80

7. 763
× 47

8. 908
× 39

9. 453 × 71

10. 674 × 85

11. 312 × 58

Name _____

Using Critical Thinking

What number multiplied by itself is 2,116?

| Find the multiples of 10 it is between. | | Choose numbers and find their product. Use a calculator. |

$40 \times 40 = 1,600$
$50 \times 50 = 2,500$

 Try 45.
Try 47.
Try 46.

$45 \times 45 = 2,025$ too small
$47 \times 47 = 2,209$ too big
$46 \times 46 = 2,116$.
The number is **46.**

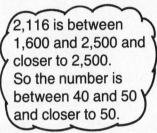 2,116 is between 1,600 and 2,500 and closer to 2,500. So the number is between 40 and 50 and closer to 50.

Find these products.

1.   10
     × 10

2.   20
     × 20

3.   30
     × 30

4.   40
     × 40

5.   50
     × 50

6.   60
     × 60

7.   70
     × 70

8.   80
     × 80

9.   90
     × 90

Each number below is the product of a number multiplied by itself. First decide what multiples of 10 it is between. Use the answers to the exercises above to help you. Then use a calculator to find the number.

10. 196

Between _____ and _____

The number is _____ .

11. 529

Between _____ and _____

The number is _____ .

12. 2,704

13. 1,444

14. 5,776

15. 3,025

_____   _____

_____   _____

Use Logical Reasoning

Terri has 28 students in her gym class. 14 of them run around the track. 18 of them jump hurdles. How many students both run and jump?

Think logically about the data.

Add how many run or jump.	Write how many students in class.	Subtract to find how many do both.

14 run + 18 jump = 32 run and/or jump

28 students

32 − 28 = **4**

4 students do both.

Use logical reasoning to solve each problem.

1. Tom has 34 students in his class. 20 of them run around the track. 18 of them throw the discus. How many do both?

How many run and/or throw? _____

How many students in class? _____

How many do both? _____

2. There are 58 students on Amy's track team. 26 of them jump hurdles. 38 of them take part in the high jump. How many do both?

3. There are 24 judges at the track meet. 13 of them judge the shot put, and 16 judge the pole vault. How many judge both events?

4. There are 12 people on the track team. During practice, 9 run the 500 meter dash. 8 run cross country. How many practice both?

5. The coach bought shirts for the 64 students on the track team. 24 of the students want yellow. 52 of them want green. How many want both colors?

Multiplying Money

You can multiply money the same way you multiply
whole numbers.

7.64×36 = ?

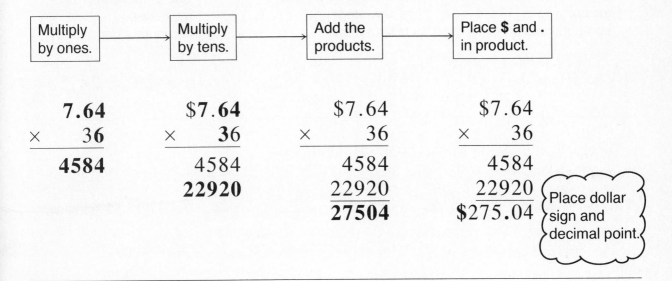

Multiply by ones.	Multiply by tens.	Add the products.	Place $ and . in product.

$$\begin{array}{r} 7.64 \\ \times\ \ \ 36 \\ \hline 4584 \end{array}$$

$$\begin{array}{r} \$7.64 \\ \times\ \ \ 36 \\ \hline 4584 \\ 22920 \end{array}$$

$$\begin{array}{r} \$7.64 \\ \times\ \ \ 36 \\ \hline 4584 \\ 22920 \\ \hline 27504 \end{array}$$

$$\begin{array}{r} \$7.64 \\ \times\ \ \ 36 \\ \hline 4584 \\ 22920 \\ \hline \$275.04 \end{array}$$

Place dollar sign and decimal point.

Find the products.

1.
$$\begin{array}{r} \$2.38 \\ \times\ \ \ 24 \end{array}$$

2.
$$\begin{array}{r} \$6.25 \\ \times\ \ \ 12 \end{array}$$

3.
$$\begin{array}{r} \$7.84 \\ \times\ \ \ 63 \end{array}$$

4.
$$\begin{array}{r} \$0.86 \\ \times\ \ \ 75 \end{array}$$

5.
$$\begin{array}{r} \$6.15 \\ \times\ \ \ 61 \end{array}$$

6.
$$\begin{array}{r} \$4.36 \\ \times\ \ \ 84 \end{array}$$

7.
$$\begin{array}{r} \$3.76 \\ \times\ \ \ 22 \end{array}$$

8.
$$\begin{array}{r} \$5.49 \\ \times\ \ \ 36 \end{array}$$

9.
$$\begin{array}{r} \$49 \\ \times\ \ \ 60 \end{array}$$

10.
$$\begin{array}{r} \$87 \\ \times\ \ \ 48 \end{array}$$

11.
$$\begin{array}{r} \$327 \\ \times\ \ \ 34 \end{array}$$

12.
$$\begin{array}{r} \$2.85 \\ \times\ \ \ 25 \end{array}$$

13. 7.29×43 = _____

14. 5.36×27 = _____

Choosing a Calculation Method

You can choose calculation methods according to the type of problem you have to solve.

Use **mental math** for easy computations.	Use **paper and pencil** for few-step computations.	Use a **calculator** for multi-step computations.
$40 \times 30 = 1,200$	$124 \times 3 = 372$	$846 \times 29 = 24,534$

Write which calculation method you would choose.
Then solve.

1. $10 \times 50 =$ _____

2. $115 \times 6 =$ _____

3. $7,437 \times 24 =$ _____

_____ _____ _____

4. $21 \times 3 =$ _____

5. $974 \times 632 =$ _____

6. $86 + 5 =$ _____

_____ _____ _____

Choose the most useful calculation method. Then solve.

7. Tom weighs 140 pounds. His brother weighs 70 pounds. How many pounds do they weigh altogether?

_____

8. Will ordered 135 boxes of pencils. Each box cost $1.75. What is the total cost?

_____

9. There are 165 pads of paper in one box. Tina has 4 boxes. How many pads of paper does Tina have?

_____

10. Geri's aunt drove 305 miles one day and 156 miles the next day. How many more miles did she drive the first day?

_____

Multiple-Step Problems

Sometimes you need to use more than 1 operation to solve a problem.

Pedro bought 4 boards. He gave the cashier $10.00. How much money should he get back?

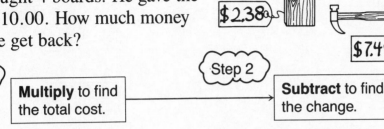

$3.26

$9.50

$2.38

$7.49

$3.95

Step 1

Multiply to find the total cost.

Step 2

Subtract to find the change.

$2.38 × 4 = $9.52

$10.00 − $9.52 = $0.48

Pedro should get $0.48 back.

Use the price signs to solve these problems.

1. Sally bought 3 pounds of nails and 1 tape measure. How much did she spend?

   Step 1: Find the cost of 3 pounds of nails.

   $$3 \times \$3.26 = \underline{\hspace{2cm}}$$

   Step 2: Add the cost of the nails and tape measure to find the total cost.

   _____ + _____ = _____

2. Pete bought a screwdriver and a hammer. He gave the clerk $20. How much change did he get back?

   Step 1: Find the cost of a screwdriver and a hammer.

   _____

   Step 2: Subract to find the change. _____

3. Tony bought 2 hammers on sale for $12.00. How much did he save?

   _____

4. Carmen bought 3 tape measures. She gave the cashier $30. How much did she get back?

   _____

Addison-Wesley | All Rights Reserved

Name _____

Telling Time: Minutes

25 minutes past 3

11 minutes to 4

Write each time.

1.

__2__ : __05__

__5__ minutes past __2__

2.

____ : ____

____ minutes past ____

3.

____ : ____

____ minutes past ____

4.

__1__ : __40__

__20__ minutes to __2__

5.

____ : ____

____ minutes to ____

6.

____ : ____

____ minutes to ____

Write each time as it would look on a digital clock.

7.

____ : ____

8.

____ : ____

9.

____ : ____

Use with text pages 206-207.

A.M. and P.M./Reading the Calendar

The hours between midnight and noon are the **a.m.** hours.

The hours between noon and midnight are the **p.m.** hours.

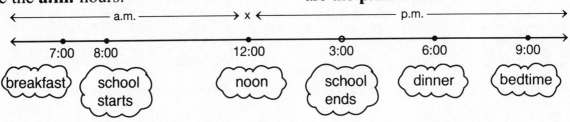

Write each time as **a.m.** or **p.m.**

1. Kao eats breakfast at

7:00 _____

2. Holly goes to school at

7:50 _____

3. Laurie gets home from school

at 3:50 _____

4. Mr. Perez cooks his supper at

5:30 _____

June is the **sixth** month of the year. Miranda has circled the 14th because it is Flag Day. It is on the second Thursday. To write dates:

JUNE 1990						
S	M	T	W	T	F	S
					1	2
3	4	5	6	7	8	9
10	11	12	13	(14)	15	16
17	18	19	20	21	22	23
24	25	26	27	28	29	30

| Write the month. | → | Write the day. | → | Write the year. |

June 14, 1990   or   6/14/90

June is the **6th** month

Use the calendar to name these dates.

5. Miranda's brother's birthday is the second Saturday. Write the date two ways.

_____

_____

6. The second Tuesday falls on what date? Write the date two ways.

_____

_____

Addison-Wesley | All Rights Reserved

Elapsed Time

To find what time an event will end, begin at the starting time.	→	Count on the number of hours, half hours, and minutes the event will last.

Count on hours:
3:00 → 4:00 → 5:00

Count on half hours: 5:00 → 5:30

The tour will last 2 hours and 30 minutes.

The tour will end at 5:30.

To find elapsed time, start at the starting time.	→	Count on to the ending time. Count hours, half hours, and minutes.

Count hours:
1:30 → 2:30 → 3:30
2 hours

Count half hours:
3:30 → 4:00   30 min.

Count minutes:
4:00 → 4:15   15 min.

The elapsed time is 2 hours and 45 minutes.

Give the ending time.

1. The show starts at 11:20. It lasts 1 hour and 40 minutes.

_____

2. The show starts at 5:30. It lasts 2 hours and 15 minutes.

_____

Give the amount of elapsed time.

3. Starting time 6:15 a.m.
Ending time 8:15 a.m.

_____

4. Starting time 4:30 p.m.
Ending time 5:15 p.m.

_____

Each event lasted 1 hour and 30 minutes. Give the ending time.

5. 6:05 _____

6. 3:15 _____

Problems with More than One Answer

When solving problems, make sure that you find all the answers. Some problems have more than one answer.

Larry bought 20 pounds of potatoes. They come in 5-pound and 10-pound bags. How many bags of each size did he buy?

List number of sentences with sums of 20.	→	Try combinations of 5s and 10s.	→	Count how many of each.

$10 + 10 = 20$ 2 10-pound bags (That works.)

$10 + 5 + 5 = 20$ 1 10-pound bags and 2 5-pound bags (That works.)

$5 + 5 + 5 + 10 = 25$ (That doesn't work.)

$5 + 5 + 5 + 5 = 20$ 4 5-pound bags (That works.)

There are three possible answers to this problem.

___

Find as many answers as you can for each problem.

1. Marika bought 10 pounds of carrots. They come in 2-pound and 5-pound bags. How many bags of each size did she buy?

List ways.	→	Number of bags

$5 + 5 = 10$ _____   _____

_____   _____

2. Linsay counted 18 wheels on the motorcycles and cars in the parking lot. How many motorcycles and how many cars were there?

List ways.

_____

_____

3. Baker bought 24 feet of ribbon. It came in 3-foot and 4-foot sections. How many of each size did he buy?

List ways.

_____

_____

Estimating and Measuring Length: Nonstandard Units

You can estimate and measure using nonstandard units.

1 span

1 cubit

1 step

Write the body unit you would use to measure each object.

1. The length of your classroom _____

2. The width of a bookcase _____

3. The height of a chalkboard _____

4. The length of a ruler _____

5. The distance between two desks _____

6. The length of a school bus _____

Choose the body unit you would use to measure. Estimate
and then measure the length of each item.

	Estimate	Measurement
7. your desktop	_____	_____
8. a closet door	_____	_____
9. a large textbook	_____	_____
10. your classroom	_____	_____

Inch, Foot, and Yard

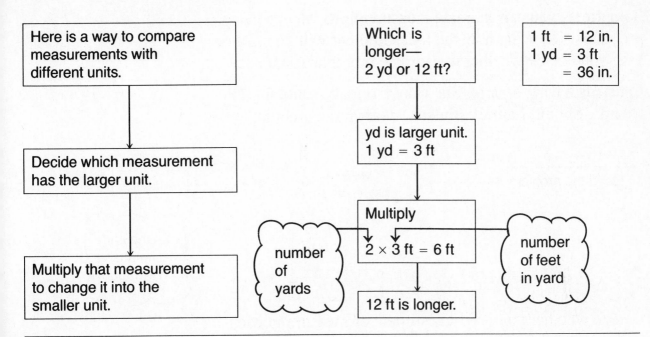

Here is a way to compare measurements with different units.	Which is longer— 2 yd or 12 ft?

1 ft = 12 in.
1 yd = 3 ft
       = 36 in.

Decide which measurement has the larger unit.

yd is larger unit.
1 yd = 3 ft

Multiply that measurement to change it into the smaller unit.

Multiply
2×3 ft = 6 ft

number of yards

number of feet in yard

12 ft is longer.

Write the missing number.

1. 4 ft = _____ in.

2. 6 ft = _____ in.

3. 4 yd = _____ ft

4. 60 in. = _____ ft

5. 6 yd = _____ ft

6. 72 in. = _____ yd

Ring the larger measurement.

7. 2 yd   3 ft   **8.** 46 in. 4 ft   **9.** 4 yd   72 in.   **10.** 7 ft   4 yd

11. 3 yd   72 in.   **12.** 3 yd   10 ft   **13.** 8 ft   48 in.   **14.** 50 in. 5 ft

Ring the object that is longer. Write **same** if the objects are the same length.

15.

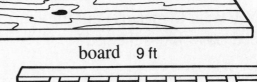

hammer   1 ft   board   9 ft

16.

board   9 ft   ladder   3 yd

Problem Solving: Deciding When to Estimate

Sometimes you can estimate measurements when solving problems. Knowing how the measurement will be used can help you decide whether to estimate or get an exact answer.

Laurie is having a party. She wants to make salad for 25 friends. Should Laurie estimate or weigh the amount?

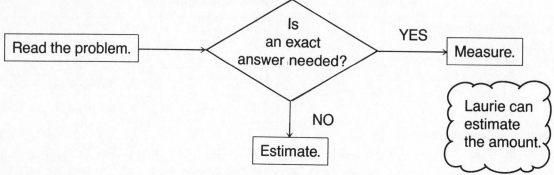

Decide whether you need to estimate or measure in each problem. Explain why.

1. You want to buy roller skates. What size should you buy?

_____

_____

2. You want to put paper on your kite frame. How big is the kite frame?

_____

_____

3. You are making a cushion for your chair. How much stuffing do you need?

_____

_____

4. You are making cheese dip for 4 friends. How much should you make?

_____

_____

5. You want to make a quilt for your bed. How big is the bed?

_____

_____

6. You are making a fence around your yard. How many feet of fence do you need?

_____

_____

Miles

Turtle Creek

Pepper

Birch

Big Rock

Big Town

Park Lake

Table Rock

Meadowlark

Stonesthrow

⊢—⊣ stands for 10 miles

This map shows some of the towns along a bus route. Use your pencil to estimate the distance between Stonesthrow and Meadowlark.

Find how many pencil ends fit between the two towns.	→	Find out what distance a pencil end stands for.	→	Multiply to find the distance in miles.

2 pencil ends

1 pencil end stands for 10 miles.

2 × 10 miles = 20

The estimated distance between the two towns is about 20 miles.

Estimate these distances in miles using your pencil end and the map above.

1. Stonesthrow to Birch

number of pencil ends _____

number of miles _____

2. Table Rock to Big Town

number of pencil ends _____

number of miles _____

3. Turtle Creek to Birch

_____

4. Pepper to Table Rock

_____

5. Park Lake to Big Town

_____

6. Big Rock to Pepper

_____

Circle the greater distance.

7. Meadowlark to Big Rock   or   Turtle Creek to Park Lake

Perimeter/Using a Benchmark

Perimeter means the distance around a figure. One way to find the perimeter of a figure is to add the lengths of the sides.

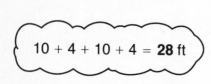

10 + 4 + 10 + 4 = **28** ft

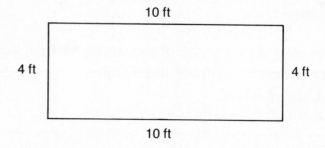

10 ft

4 ft   4 ft

10 ft

The perimeter is 28 ft.

Find the perimeter.

1.

8 ft

3 ft   3 ft

8 ft

2.

12 in.

20 in.   20 in.

12 in.

Look for an object that is about 1 inch in length. Using that length as a **benchmark,** you can estimate length and width.

3.

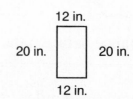

length ___1 in.___

width _____

perimeter _____

Use your own benchmark to estimate the length, width, and perimeter of these objects. Check your estimates by measuring with a ruler.

4. your math textbook   _____

5. a sheet of paper   _____

6. an envelope   _____

Addison-Wesley | All Rights Reserved

Problem Solving: Data from a Chart

A chart is a way to organize data. The chart below describes
4 passenger ocean liners.

Ship	Length	Width	Passengers
Queen Elizabeth II	963 ft	105 ft	2,025
Canberra	818 ft	102 ft	2,400
Oriana	804 ft	97 ft	2,216
United States	990 ft	102 ft	1,930

What is the difference between the length of the *Canberra*
and the length of the *Oriana?*

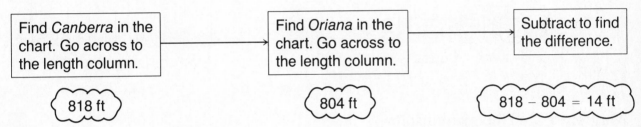

Find *Canberra* in the chart. Go across to the length column.	→	Find *Oriana* in the chart. Go across to the length column.	→	Subtract to find the difference.
818 ft		804 ft		818 − 804 = 14 ft

The *Canberra* is 14 feet longer.

_____

Solve using data from the chart above.

1. How much wider is the widest
ship than the narrowest?

widest ship _____105 ft_____

narrowest ship _____

difference _____

2. The length of the *Rotterdam* is
848 ft. How much longer is this
than the *Canberra?*

_____

3. Does the widest ship carry the
most passengers?

_____

4. What is the total passenger
capacity for the *Canberra* and the
United States?

_____

Estimating and Measuring Capacity

1 pint = 2 cups

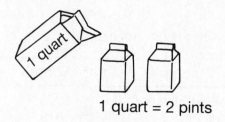

1 quart = 2 pints

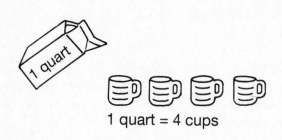

1 quart = 4 cups

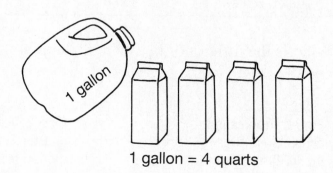

1 gallon = 4 quarts

Multiply to find the relationships.

1. 1 gallon = 4 quarts, so

2 gallons = __8__ quarts   (2 times as many)

2. 1 quart = 4 cups, so

3 quarts = __12__ cups   (3 times as many)

3. 1 quart = 2 pints, so

2 quarts = _____ pints   (2 times as many)

4. 1 pint = 2 cups, so

3 pints = _____ cups

5. 1 quart = 4 cups, so

2 quarts = _____ cups

6. 1 quart = 2 pints, so

3 quarts = _____ pints

Ring the better estimate.

7. water in a sink

5 pints or (5 gallons)

8. water in an aquarium

10 cups or 10 gallons

9. full glass of milk

2 cups or 2 pints

10. juice in a pitcher

2 cups or 2 quarts

Estimating and Measuring Weight/ Temperature: Degrees Fahrenheit

Weight

Which weighs more?

Change 3 pounds to ounces.

1 lb = 16 oz, therefore
3 lb = 3 × 16 oz = 48 oz

Compare 11 oz < 48 oz

The apples weigh more.

Ring the item that weighs more.

1. Nails 1 lb
   Hammer 22 oz

2. Drill 3 lb
   Wrench 22 oz

3. Saw 6 lb
   Sander 78 oz

4. Dictionary 4 lb
   Book 36 oz

Estimate the weight of these items in pounds.

5.

6.

Temperature

Degrees Fahrenheit (°F)

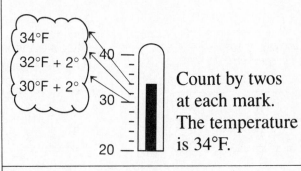

34°F
32°F + 2°
30°F + 2°

Count by twos at each mark. The temperature is 34°F.

Write each temperature.

7.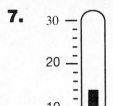

8.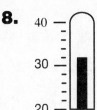

9.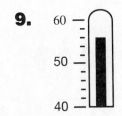

10.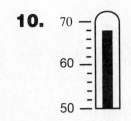

11.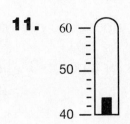

12.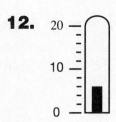

Name _____

Understanding Division

Division takes place when a total is separated into groups.

Toma has 12 eggs to divide among his 6 family members.
How many eggs will each person get?

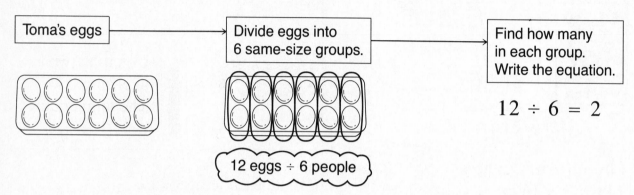

| Toma's eggs | → | Divide eggs into 6 same-size groups. | → | Find how many in each group. Write the equation. |

12 eggs ÷ 6 people

$$12 \div 6 = 2$$

Toma has 6 groups with 2 eggs in each group. Each family member will get 2 eggs.

Use counters to find the answer. Ring each group. Write the equation.

1. It takes 10 people to wash 2 elephants. How many people are needed for each elephant?

 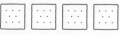 $10 \div 2 = $ _____

2. You have 16 crackers. There are 4 people.

How many crackers does each person get? _____

3. The tape case holds 24 tapes in 3 equal rows.

How many tapes are in each row? _____

Relating Multiplication and Division

3 rows of 6 is 18.

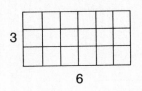

3

6

Fact Family

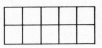
$3 \times 6 = 18$ $6 \times 3 = 18$

$18 \div 6 = 3$ $18 \div 3 = 6$

1. Write the fact family for this: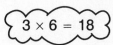

_____   _____

_____   _____

Use the graph paper to help you find the missing factor.

2. $16 \div 2 = $ _____

3. $16 \div 8 = $ _____

Divide. Think about finding the missing factor.

4. $28 \div 7 = $ _____

5. $32 \div 4 = $ _____

6. $25 \div 5 = $ _____

7. $56 \div 8 = $ _____

8. $36 \div 9 = $ _____

9. $21 \div 3 = $ _____

Give three more equations in each fact family.

10. $6 \times 4 = 24$ _____ _____ _____

11. $3 \times 9 = 27$ _____ _____ _____

12. $7 \times 6 = 42$ _____ _____ _____

13. $5 \times 8 = 40$ _____ _____ _____

Addison-Wesley | All rights reserved

Dividing by 2 and 3

Use a multiplication equation to find a quotient.

24 ÷ 3 = ___?___

Think:

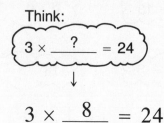

3 × ___?___ = 24

↓

3 × ___8___ = 24

| 24 ÷ 3 = 8 |

$\overset{?}{2)\overline{10}}$

Think:

2 × ___?___ = 10

↓

2 × ___5___ = 10

| $\overset{5}{2)\overline{10}}$ |

Divide. Use a multiplication equation to check.

1. 12 ÷ 3 = _____   **2.** 8 ÷ 2 = _____   **3.** 21 ÷ 3 = _____

4. 15 ÷ 3 = _____   **5.** 2 ÷ 2 = _____   **6.** 24 ÷ 3 = _____

7. 14 ÷ 2 = _____   **8.** 16 ÷ 2 = _____   **9.** 6 ÷ 2 = _____

Find the quotients.

10. 6 ÷ 2 = _____   **11.** 14 ÷ 2 = _____   **12.** 18 ÷ 2 = _____

13. 16 ÷ 2 = _____   **14.** 24 ÷ 3 = _____   **15.** 15 ÷ 3 = _____

16. 6 ÷ 3 = _____   **17.** 12 ÷ 6 = _____   **18.** 9 ÷ 3 = _____

19. 2)$\overline{12}$ = _____   **20.** 3)$\overline{12}$ = _____   **21.** 4)$\overline{24}$ = _____

22. 2)$\overline{8}$ = _____   **23.** 3)$\overline{21}$ = _____   **24.** 2)$\overline{18}$ = _____

25. 3)$\overline{27}$ = _____   **26.** 3)$\overline{15}$ = _____   **27.** 3)$\overline{12}$ = _____

Name _____

Dividing by 4 and 5

A fact family has four facts. Each fact uses the same three numbers.

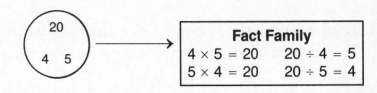

Fact Family

$4 \times 5 = 20$ $20 \div 4 = 5$
$5 \times 4 = 20$ $20 \div 5 = 4$

Use fact families or missing factors to help find a quotient.

Examples:

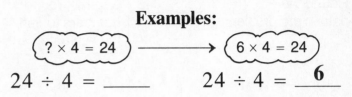

$? \times 4 = 24$ ⟶ $6 \times 4 = 24$

$24 \div 4 = \underline{\hspace{1cm}}$ $24 \div 4 = \underline{\hspace{0.3cm}6\hspace{0.3cm}}$

Solve.

| 12 |
| 3   4 |

1. $3 \times 4 = \underline{12}$ $12 \div 4 = \underline{3}$

$4 \times 3 = \underline{\hspace{1cm}}$ $12 \div 3 = \underline{\hspace{1cm}}$

| 15 |
| 3   5 |

2. $3 \times 5 = \underline{\hspace{1cm}}$ $15 \div 5 = \underline{\hspace{1cm}}$

$5 \times 3 = \underline{\hspace{1cm}}$ $15 \div 3 = \underline{\hspace{1cm}}$

Divide.

$? \times 4 = 8$

3. $8 \div 4 = \underline{\hspace{1cm}}$

$? \times 5 = 10$

4. $10 \div 5 = \underline{\hspace{1cm}}$

$? \times 4 = 20$

5. $20 \div 4 = \underline{\hspace{1cm}}$

6. $36 \div 4 = \underline{\hspace{1cm}}$

7. $35 \div 5 = \underline{\hspace{1cm}}$

8. $16 \div 4 = \underline{\hspace{1cm}}$

9. $40 \div 5 = \underline{\hspace{1cm}}$

10. $32 \div 4 = \underline{\hspace{1cm}}$

11. $24 \div 4 = \underline{\hspace{1cm}}$

12. $45 \div 5 = \underline{\hspace{1cm}}$

13. $4 \div 4 = \underline{\hspace{1cm}}$

14. $20 \div 5 = \underline{\hspace{1cm}}$

15. $4 \overline{)16}$

16. $5 \overline{)35}$

17. $4 \overline{)12}$

18. $4 \overline{)28}$

19. $4 \overline{)36}$

20. $5 \overline{)5}$

21. $4 \overline{)4}$

22. $4 \overline{)32}$

Estimate the Answer

The bear weighs 377 pounds and the tiger weighs
283 pounds. How much more does the bear weigh?

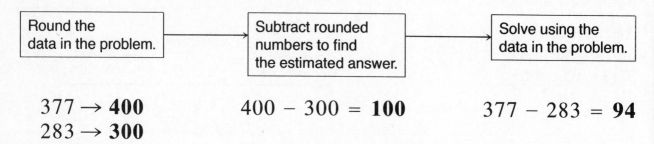

| Round the data in the problem. | → | Subtract rounded numbers to find the estimated answer. | → | Solve using the data in the problem. |

$$377 \rightarrow \mathbf{400}$$
$$283 \rightarrow \mathbf{300}$$

$$400 - 300 = \mathbf{100}$$

$$377 - 283 = \mathbf{94}$$

94 is a reasonable solution because it is close to the estimated answer, 100.

Use estimation to decide which answer is most reasonable.
Ring that answer.

1. Min sold drinks at the fair. He sold
775 cups Saturday and 515 cups
Sunday. How many cups did he sell?

   A. 1,190 cups
   B. 1,290 cups   (800 + 500 = 1,300)
   C. 1,390 cups

2. Sally bought 24 cans of juice.
Each can cost $0.98. How much
money did the cans cost?

   A. $23.52
   B. $25.52
   C. $26.52

Estimate the answer. Then solve the problem. Decide if your
answer is reasonable.

3. A new chair costs $199.84.
Ramon has saved $54.36. How
much more money does he need?

_____

4. Ana pays $14 a month for her
stereo. How much is this per year?

_____

5. Hilo buys tapes in packages of 4.
Each package cost $18. How
much would 20 tapes cost?

_____

6. Johana was born was born in
1982. When she was 8, she
received a new bike. What year
was that?

_____

0 and 1 in Division

Here are some special 0 and 1 properties in division:

 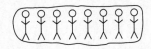 ⓪⓪⓪⓪⓪⓪⓪⓪⓪

a. $8 \div 8 = 1$

The quotient of a number divided by itself is 1.

b. $8 \div 1 = 8$

The quotient of a number divided by 1 is that number.

c. $0 \div 8 = 0$

Zero divided by any number is 0.

$8 \div 0 =$

This does not make sense.

Find these quotients. Then think of the property you used and write the letter next to your answer.

1. $9 \div 1 = \underline{9} \quad \underline{b}$

2. $0 \div 76 = \underline{\quad} \quad \underline{\quad}$

3. $14 \div 14 = \underline{\quad} \quad \underline{\quad}$

4. $82 \div 1 = \underline{\quad} \quad \underline{\quad}$

Find the quotients.

5. $3 \div 3 = \underline{\quad}$

6. $4 \div 1 = \underline{\quad}$

7. $0 \div 12 = \underline{\quad}$

8. $0 \div 21 = \underline{\quad}$

9. $28 \div 28 = \underline{\quad}$

10. $18 \div 1 = \underline{\quad}$

11. $54 \div 54 = \underline{\quad}$

12. $0 \div 34 = \underline{\quad}$

13. $19 \div 1 = \underline{\quad}$

14. $25 \div 1 = \underline{\quad}$

15. $65 \div 65 = \underline{\quad}$

16. $80 \div 1 = \underline{\quad}$

17. $0 \div 17 = \underline{\quad}$

18. $76 \div 1 = \underline{\quad}$

19. $0 \div 29 = \underline{\quad}$

20. $79 \div 79 = \underline{\quad}$

21. $0 \div 62 = \underline{\quad}$

22. $42 \div 42 = \underline{\quad}$

Dividing by 6 and 7

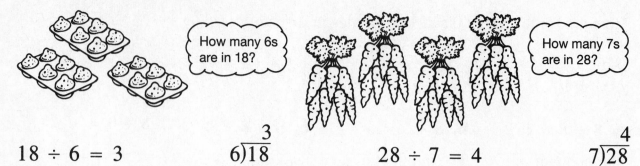

How many 6s are in 18?

How many 7s are in 28?

$18 \div 6 = 3$ $6\overline{)18}$ with 3 above $28 \div 7 = 4$ $7\overline{)28}$ with 4 above

---

Divide. Use these pictures to help you.

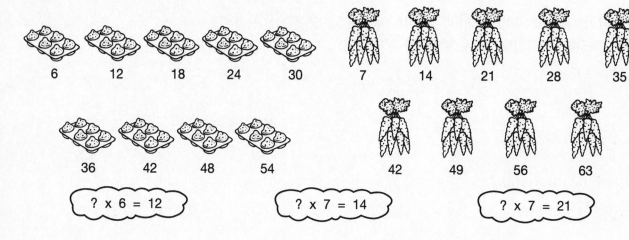

6   12   18   24   30   7   14   21   28   35

36   42   48   54   42   49   56   63

? x 6 = 12   ? x 7 = 14   ? x 7 = 21

1. $12 \div 6 = \underline{2}$ **2.** $14 \div 7 = \underline{}$ **3.** $21 \div 7 = \underline{}$

4. $48 \div 6 = \underline{}$ **5.** $35 \div 7 = \underline{}$ **6.** $6 \div 6 = \underline{}$

7. $36 \div 6 = \underline{}$ **8.** $56 \div 7 = \underline{}$ **9.** $30 \div 6 = \underline{}$

10. $7\overline{)21}$ **11.** $6\overline{)24}$ **12.** $7\overline{)28}$ **13.** $7\overline{)14}$

14. $7\overline{)49}$ **15.** $6\overline{)42}$ **16.** $6\overline{)36}$ **17.** $7\overline{)56}$

Name _____

Dividing by 8 and 9

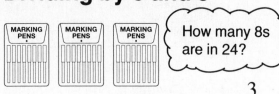 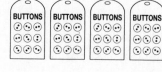

How many 8s are in 24?

$$24 \div 8 = 3$$

$$8\overline{)24} \quad \overset{3}{}$$

How many 9s are in 36?

$$36 \div 9 = 4$$

$$9\overline{)36} \quad \overset{4}{}$$

Divide. Use these pictures to help you.

8   16   24   32   40

9   18   27   36   45

48   56   64   72

54   63   72   81

eights   nines

$? \times 8 = 16$ $? \times 9 = 27$ $? \times 8 = 48$

1. $16 \div 8 = \underline{\quad 2 \quad}$ **2.** $27 \div 9 = \underline{\quad\quad}$ **3.** $48 \div 8 = \underline{\quad\quad}$

4. $24 \div 3 = \underline{\quad\quad}$ **5.** $18 \div 9 = \underline{\quad\quad}$ **6.** $40 \div 8 = \underline{\quad\quad}$

7. $36 \div 9 = \underline{\quad\quad}$ **8.** $32 \div 8 = \underline{\quad\quad}$ **9.** $54 \div 9 = \underline{\quad\quad}$

10. $64 \div 8 = \underline{\quad\quad}$ **11.** $81 \div 9 = \underline{\quad\quad}$ **12.** $8 \div 8 = \underline{\quad\quad}$

13. $8\overline{)64}$ **14.** $9\overline{)27}$ **15.** $8\overline{)72}$ **16.** $8\overline{)32}$

Using Critical Thinking

When the number 12 is put in the Function Machine, the machine adds 2 to it, and 14 (12 + 2) comes out.

If 16 is put in the machine, what number will come out?
18 will come out.

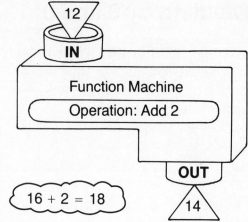

Add 2	
IN	OUT
16	18

16 + 2 = 18

Write the numbers that come out of the machine.

1.

Add 6	
IN	OUT
4	10
12	
26	

2.

Subtract 7	
IN	OUT
9	
15	
18	

3.

Multiply by 3	
IN	OUT
4	
7	
12	

Write the correct number in the box.

4.

Divide by ☐	
IN	OUT
16	4
12	3
8	2

5.

Multiply by ☐	
IN	OUT
3	18
2	12
1	6

6.

Subtract ☐	
IN	OUT
12	3
18	9
21	12

Write the operation rule in the box.

7.

IN	OUT
21	7
15	5
9	3

8.

IN	OUT
5	10
9	14
10	15

9.

IN	OUT
3	12
5	20
9	36

Use with text page 254.

Name _____

Work Backward

To solve a problem, you may have to start at the end of the problem and work backward.

Jamal was given his allowance on Friday. On Saturday, he spent $3. On Monday, Laura paid Jamal the $5 she owed him. If Jamal now has $6, how much is his allowance?

Subtract to find how much Jamal had before Laura paid him.

$$\$6 - \$5 = \$1$$

Add back what he spent to the $1 to find his allowance.

$$\$1 + \$3 = \$4$$

Jamal's allowance is $4.

Work backward to solve these problems.

1. Pedro bought 5 records. Each record cost $6. Then he spent $7 for a tape. He had $2 left. How much money did Pedro have in the beginning?

How much does Pedro have left?

_2_

Add back what he spent on

the tape. $ _2_ + _____ = _____

How much did he spend on the records?

$ _5_ × _6_ = $ _____

How much did he have in the beginning?

$ _____ + $ _____ = $ _____

2. Larry took all the books out of the bookcase. He put 14 books on one table. Then he put the rest on another table in 6 stacks of 7. How many books were in the bookcase when he started?

_____

3. Geena put 15 stamps on one page. She put the rest on 4 pages of 9 each. How many stamps are in her stamp book?

_____

Quotients and Remainders

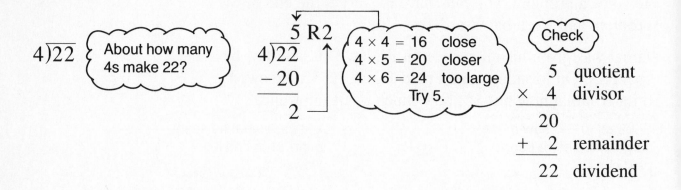

$4\overline{)22}$ **About how many 4s make 22?**

$$\begin{array}{r} 5\ R2 \\ 4\overline{)22} \\ -20 \\ \hline 2 \end{array}$$

$4 \times 4 = 16$ close
$4 \times 5 = 20$ closer
$4 \times 6 = 24$ too large
Try 5.

Check

$$\begin{array}{r} 5 \quad \text{quotient} \\ \times \ 4 \quad \text{divisor} \\ \hline 20 \\ + \ 2 \quad \text{remainder} \\ \hline 22 \quad \text{dividend} \end{array}$$

An artist donated 25 books to Ray School. It has not been decided how many classes will share the books. Complete the chart. You may use counters.

	Number of Classes Sharing the Books	Number of Books for Each Class	Number of Books Left Over
1.	3		
2.	4		
3.	5		
4.	6		
5.	7		
6.	8		
7.	9		

Use the chart above to help you find each quotient and remainder. Multiply and add to check.

8. $4\overline{)25}$ **9.** $5\overline{)25}$ **10.** $8\overline{)25}$

11. $6\overline{)25}$ **12.** $9\overline{)25}$ **13.** $7\overline{)25}$

Name _____

Special Quotients

| To find 240 ÷ 6 |→| find 24 ÷ 6 |→| then multiply by 10. |

$\{4\}$ $\{4 \times 10 = 40\} \rightarrow \{240 ÷ 6 = 40\}$

$\{$ Check: $6 \times 40 = 240\}$

Find the quotients. Check your answers by multiplying.

1. $60 ÷ 3 =$ _____
Check:

$3 \times$ ____ = ____

2. $40 ÷ 4 =$ _____

$4 \times$ ____ = ____

3. $120 ÷ 6 =$ _____

$6 \times$ ____ = ____

4. $240 ÷ 8 =$ _____
Check:

$8 \times$ ____ = ____

5. $150 ÷ 3 =$ _____

$3 \times$ ____ = ____

6. $720 ÷ 9 =$ _____

$9 \times$ ____ = ____

7. $90 ÷ 3 =$ _____
Check:

$3 \times$ ____ = ____

8. $80 ÷ 8 =$ _____

$8 \times$ ____ = ____

9. $140 ÷ 7 =$ _____

$7 \times$ ____ = ____

10. $350 ÷ 5 =$ _____
Check:

$5 \times$ ____ = ____

11. $450 ÷ 9 =$ _____

$9 \times$ ____ = ____

12. $640 ÷ 8 =$ _____

$8 \times$ ____ = ____

Estimating Quotients

You can estimate a quotient by rounding and dividing.

Estimate to the nearest ten.	Estimate to the nearest ten.	Estimate to the nearest dollar.

$$46 \div 5 \qquad\qquad 322 \div 4 \qquad\qquad \$11.75 \div 6$$

46 is close to 50. $\quad 50 \div 5 = 10 \qquad\qquad 320 \div 4 = 80 \qquad\qquad \$12 \div 6 = \$2$

About 10 $\qquad\qquad$ About 80 $\qquad\qquad$ About $2

Round to the nearest ten and divide.

Round 77 to 80.　　　　　　　　　Round 123 to 120.

1. $77 \div 2 \rightarrow \underline{80} \div \underline{2} = \underline{40}$　　　　**2.** $123 \div 3 \rightarrow \underline{120} \div \underline{3} = \underline{}$

3. $57 \div 2 \rightarrow \underline{} \div \underline{2} = \underline{}$　　　　**4.** $89 \div 3 \rightarrow \underline{} \div \underline{} = \underline{}$

5. $78 \div 4 \rightarrow \underline{} \div \underline{} = \underline{}$　　　　**6.** $43 \div 4 \rightarrow \underline{} \div \underline{} = \underline{}$

7. $147 \div 5 \rightarrow \underline{} \div \underline{} = \underline{}$　　　　**8.** $241 \div 6 \rightarrow \underline{} \div \underline{} = \underline{}$

9. $634 \div 7 \rightarrow \underline{} \div \underline{} = \underline{}$　　　　**10.** $110 \div 4 \rightarrow \underline{} \div \underline{} = \underline{}$

Round to the nearest dollar and divide. Write whether the estimate is **over** or **under** the exact quotient.

Round to $6.

11. $\$5.75 \div 3 \rightarrow \underline{\$6} \div \underline{3} = \underline{\$2} \qquad \underline{over}$

12. $\$14.10 \div 2 \rightarrow \underline{} \div \underline{2} = \underline{} \qquad \underline{}$

13. $\$29.95 \div 6 \rightarrow \underline{} \div \underline{} = \underline{} \qquad \underline{}$

Name _____

Dividing Whole Numbers: Making the Connection

Divide 57 into 4 groups.

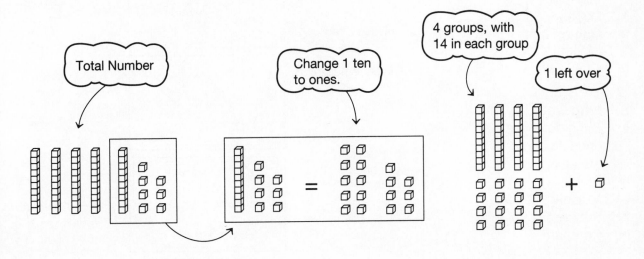

Total Number

Change 1 ten to ones.

4 groups, with 14 in each group

1 left over

Use blocks to help you complete the chart.

	Total Number	Groups	Number in Each Group	Number Left Over
1.	57	4	14	1
2.	12	4		
3.	33	5		
4.	19	2		
5.	25	5		
6.	37		6	1
7.	49		7	
8.	24		6	
9.	66		11	

RS-4 **99**

Addison-Wesley | All Rights Reserved

Dividing Whole Numbers: 2-Digit Quotients

Dividing Tens
- ▶ Divide
- ▶ Multiply
- ▶ Subtract
- ▶ Compare

Dividing Ones
- ▶ Bring down the ones next to the tens.
- ▶ Divide
- ▶ Multiply
- ▶ Subtract
- ▶ Compare

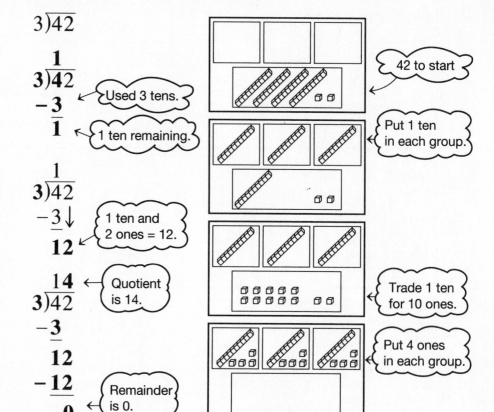

$$3\overline{)42}$$

$$\begin{array}{r} 1 \\ 3\overline{)42} \\ -3 \\ \hline 1 \end{array}$$ Used 3 tens. 1 ten remaining.

$$\begin{array}{r} 1 \\ 3\overline{)42} \\ -3\downarrow \\ \hline 12 \end{array}$$ 1 ten and 2 ones = 12.

$$\begin{array}{r} 14 \\ 3\overline{)42} \\ -3 \\ \hline 12 \\ -12 \\ \hline 0 \end{array}$$ Quotient is 14. Remainder is 0.

42 to start

Put 1 ten in each group.

Trade 1 ten for 10 ones.

Put 4 ones in each group.

Divide. Write the quotients and remainders.

1.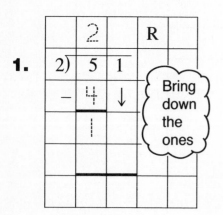

2. $6\overline{)78}$

3. $4\overline{)93}$

4. $2\overline{)57}$

5. $3\overline{)68}$

6. $5\overline{)90}$

7. $8\overline{)95}$

Interpreting Remainders

Jane bought 50 apples. A bag holds 8 apples.

Questions:

> How many bags can Jane fill completely?

> How many bags does Jane need to get all 50 apples home?

> How many apples are in the bag that is not full?

2 apples remain.

$$\begin{array}{r} 6\ \text{R2} \\ 8)\overline{50} \\ -48 \\ \hline 2 \end{array}$$

Answers:

> Jane can completely fill 6 bags.

> Jane needs 7 bags.

> There are 2 apples in the bag that is not full.

All three problems use the same division, but they have different answers.

___

Ring the correct answer.

1. John bought 64 pear trees. His truck can hold 6 trees. How many trips will the truck have to make to get all the trees home?

  A 10 trips   **B** 11 trips   **C** 4 trips

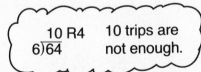

      10 R4   10 trips are
      6)64   not enough.

2. Peg has $15 to spend on strawberry plants. Each plant costs $2. How much money will Peg have after she buys the plants?

  A $7   **B** $8   **C** $1

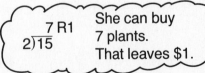

       7 R1   She can buy
     2)15   7 plants.
             That leaves $1.

3. Patrick is making peach pies. He has 35 peaches and needs 8 for each pie. How many pies can he make?

  A 4 pies   **B** 5 pies   **C** 3 pies

4. Jack has 58 melons to take to market. He can fit 5 melons in a box. How many boxes will he need to get all the melons to market?

  A 11 boxes   **B** 12 boxes
  C 3 boxes

3-Digit Quotients

Dividing Hundreds	Dividing Tens	Dividing Ones
▶ Divide ▶ Multiply ▶ Subtract ▶ Compare	▶ Bring down the tens ▶ Divide ▶ Multiply ▶ Subtract ▶ Compare	▶ Bring down the ones ▶ Divide ▶ Multiply ▶ Subtract ▶ Compare

$$
\begin{array}{r}
1 \\
4\overline{)735} \\
-4 \\
\hline
3
\end{array}
\qquad
\begin{array}{r}
18 \\
4\overline{)735} \\
-4\downarrow \\
\hline
33 \\
-32 \\
\hline
1
\end{array}
\qquad
\begin{array}{r}
183 \text{ R3} \\
4\overline{)735} \\
-4 \\
\hline
33 \\
-32\downarrow \\
\hline
15 \\
-12 \\
\hline
3
\end{array}
$$

Divide.

1.
$$
\begin{array}{r}
28 \text{ R} \\
3\overline{)853} \\
-6\downarrow \\
\hline
25 \\
-24 \\
\hline
13
\end{array}
$$
Divide ones.

2.
$$
\begin{array}{r}
4 \text{ R} \\
2\overline{)975} \\
-8\downarrow \\
\hline
17
\end{array}
$$

3. $4\overline{)563}$

4. $3\overline{)986}$

5. $2\overline{)735}$

Finding Averages

Tina exercised 14 minutes on Monday, 18 minutes on Tuesday, and 31 minutes on Wednesday. Suppose Tina exercised the same total number of minutes by exercising an equal number of minutes every day. How many minutes would Tina exercise each day?

The number of minutes Tina would be exercising each day is called the **average**.

To find the average:

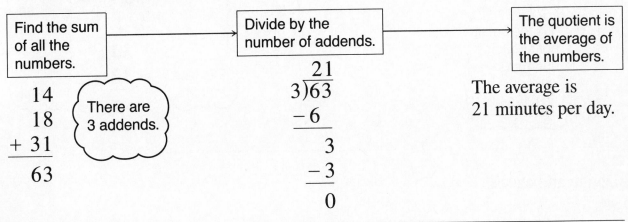

| Find the sum of all the numbers. | Divide by the number of addends. | The quotient is the average of the numbers. |

There are 3 addends.

$$\begin{array}{r} 14 \\ 18 \\ + 31 \\ \hline 63 \end{array}$$

$$\begin{array}{r} 21 \\ 3\overline{)63} \\ -6 \\ \hline 3 \\ -3 \\ \hline 0 \end{array}$$

The average is 21 minutes per day.

Find the average of these numbers. Show your work.

1. 47, 23, 38 _____

2. 62, 41, 77 _____

3. 36, 10, 45, 33 _____

4. 21, 36, 14, 13 _____

5. 121, 116, 132 _____

6. 214, 376, 148 _____

Addison-Wesley | All Rights Reserved

Name _____

Deciding Where to Start

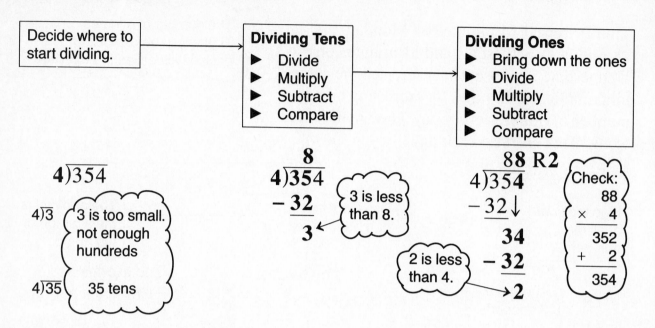

| Decide where to start dividing. | → | **Dividing Tens**
▶ Divide
▶ Multiply
▶ Subtract
▶ Compare | → | **Dividing Ones**
▶ Bring down the ones
▶ Divide
▶ Multiply
▶ Subtract
▶ Compare |

$4\overline{)354}$

$4\overline{)3}$ — 3 is too small. not enough hundreds

$4\overline{)35}$ — 35 tens

$\begin{array}{r} 8 \\ 4\overline{)354} \\ -32 \\ \hline 3 \end{array}$ 3 is less than 8.

$\begin{array}{r} 88 \text{ R2} \\ 4\overline{)354} \\ -32\downarrow \\ \hline 34 \\ -32 \\ \hline 2 \end{array}$ 2 is less than 4.

Check:
$\begin{array}{r} 88 \\ \times \quad 4 \\ \hline 352 \\ + \quad 2 \\ \hline 354 \end{array}$

Divide and check.

1.
$\begin{array}{r} 6 \quad R \\ 8\overline{)531} \\ -48\downarrow \\ \hline 51 \\ - \\ \hline \end{array}$

Check:
$\begin{array}{r} 66 \\ \times \quad 8 \\ \hline \\ + \quad 3 \end{array}$

2.
$\begin{array}{r} 6 \quad R \\ 6\overline{)376} \\ -36\downarrow \\ \hline \\ - \\ \hline \end{array}$

Check:
$\times \quad 6$

3. $7\overline{)483}$ Check: **4.** $2\overline{)195}$ Check: **5.** $4\overline{)382}$ Check:

Zero in the Quotient

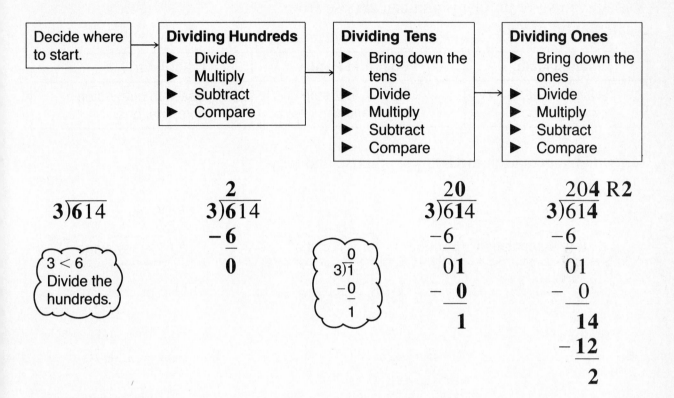

Decide where to start.

Dividing Hundreds
▶ Divide
▶ Multiply
▶ Subtract
▶ Compare

Dividing Tens
▶ Bring down the tens
▶ Divide
▶ Multiply
▶ Subtract
▶ Compare

Dividing Ones
▶ Bring down the ones
▶ Divide
▶ Multiply
▶ Subtract
▶ Compare

$$3\overline{)614}$$

$3 < 6$
Divide the hundreds.

$$\begin{array}{r} 2 \\ 3\overline{)614} \\ -6 \\ \hline 0 \end{array}$$

$$\begin{array}{r} 0 \\ 3\overline{)1} \\ -0 \\ \hline 1 \end{array}$$

$$\begin{array}{r} 20 \\ 3\overline{)614} \\ -6 \\ \hline 01 \\ -\;0 \\ \hline 1 \end{array}$$

$$\begin{array}{r} 204\ \text{R2} \\ 3\overline{)614} \\ -6 \\ \hline 01 \\ -\;0 \\ \hline 14 \\ -12 \\ \hline 2 \end{array}$$

Divide and check.

1.
$$\begin{array}{r} 8 \\ 5\overline{)403} \\ -40 \\ \hline 03 \\ -00 \\ \hline 3 \end{array}$$
Divide ones.

2.
$$\begin{array}{r} 4\overline{)413} \\ -4 \\ \hline 01 \end{array}$$
Divide tens.

3.
$$\begin{array}{r} 6\overline{)784} \\ -6 \\ \hline 18 \end{array}$$

4. $3\overline{)320}$

5. $9\overline{)450}$

6. $4\overline{)483}$

Choosing a Calculation Method

To help you solve problems you can choose from
3 calculation methods.

Mental Math	Paper and Pencil	Calculator
Use with easy computations.	Use with few-step computations.	Use with many-step computations.

Tell which calculation method you choose and why.
Then solve.

1. $36 + 14 =$ _____

easy computation

Use _____

2. $381 \div 3 =$ _____

few steps

Use _____

3. $76 \times 24 =$ _____

many steps

Use _____

4. $7 \times 23 =$ _____

5. $427 \times 641 =$ _____

6. $\$73 - \$24.76 =$ _____

7. $25 + 76 =$ _____

8. $128 - 48 =$ _____

9. $756 \div 21 =$ _____

Solve. Choose the most useful calculation method.

10. It took Sidney 54 minutes one day to deliver papers and 47 minutes the second day. How much longer did it take him the first day?

11. Juanita has 75 papers to deliver each day. How many papers does she deliver in 31 days?

Dividing with Money

You can divide with money in the same way you divide with whole numbers.

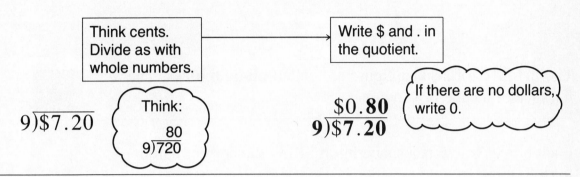

Divide. Show dollars and cents.

1. 4)$6.40

2. 8)$8.08

3. 7)$5.67

4. 8)$3.68

5. 6)$7.26

6. 3)$9.99

7. 5)$5.25

8. 2)$7.50

9. 7)$0.56

Name _____

Space Figures and Plane Figures

Many objects we see every day are shaped like these **space figures.**

  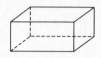

The flat faces of a space figure are called **plane figures.** The flat face of a cube is a square.

Each object below is a space figure. Ring the correct name for the figure.

1.   sphere   pyramid   cylinder

2.   cone   cylinder   rectangular prism

3.   pyramid   cone   triangular prism

4. 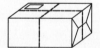   pyramid   cylinder   rectangular prism

Shade one flat face on each space figure. Name each face you shade.

5.   **6.**   **7.**

_____   _____   _____

Name _____

Polygons and Angles

A **polygon** is a figure whose sides are straight. An angle of a polygon may be less than 90°, equal to 90°, or more than 90°.

Write how many sides each figure has.

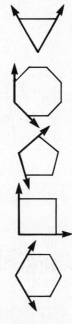

1. A triangle has _____ sides.

2. An octagon has _____ sides.

3. A pentagon has _____ sides.

4. A quadrilateral has _____ sides.

5. A hexagon has _____ sides.

Use a right angle protractor to decide if the dark angle is less than 90°, more than 90°, or equal to 90°. Ring the answer.

6. 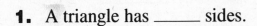 less than 90° more than 90° equal to 90°

7. 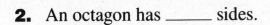 less than 90° more than 90° equal to 90°

8. 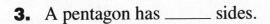 less than 90° more than 90° equal to 90°

9. 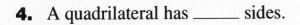 less than 90° more than 90° equal to 90°

10. 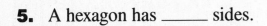 less than 90° more than 90° equal to 90°

Addison-Wesley | All Rights Reserved

Name _____

Analyzing Polygons: Parallel and Perpendicular Lines

Two lines that never meet are called **parallel** lines.	Two lines that meet in a right angle are called **perpendicular** lines.

A   C   E   B   D

Write the letter of the figure described.

1. a polygon with 1 pair of parallel sides _____

2. a quadrilateral with no parallel or perpendicular sides _____

3. a polygon with 1 pair of perpendicular sides _____

4. a polygon with 2 pairs of parallel sides _____

5. Ring the quadrilateral with 2 pairs of parallel sides.

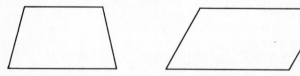

6. Ring the triangle with a pair of perpendicular sides.

 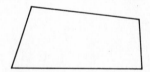

7. Ring the quadrilateral with 2 pairs of perpendicular sides.

Name _____

Symmetric Figures

This paper is folded along its line of symmetry.	The two parts of the figure fit exactly on each other.	The open figure shows **the line of symmetry.**

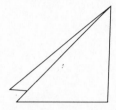 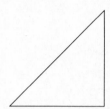 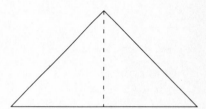

Draw what you think these figures will look like when cut
and unfolded. Draw a line of symmetry on each unfolded

figure.

1.

2.

3.

4.

5.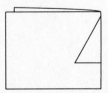

Addison-Wesley | All Rights Reserved

Name _____

Classifying Angles and Triangles

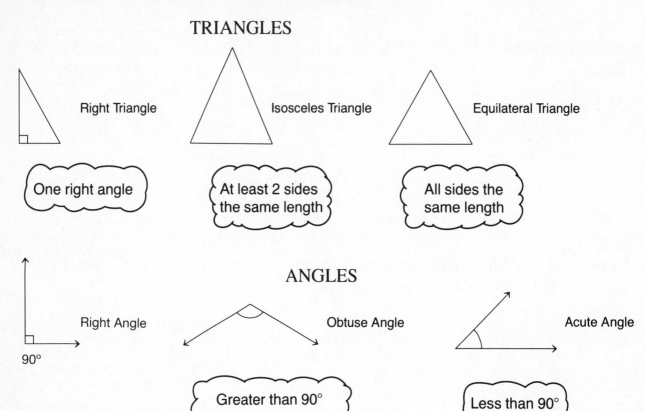

Write the name for each triangle. Then color each
acute angle red and each obtuse angle blue.

1.

A. _____

2.

B. _____

3.

C. _____

Write the letter of triangle that matches the description.

4. _____ has a right angle.

5. _____ has an obtuse angle and two sides the same length.

6. _____ has 3 acute angles and 3 sides the same length.

Name _____

Classifying Quadrilaterals

Square

(All sides the same length)

(All angles right angles)

Rectangle

(Two pairs of same-length sides)

(All angles right angles)

Trapezoid

(Exactly one pair of parallel sides)

Parallelogram

(Two pairs of same-length sides)

(Two pairs of parallel sides)

Find the quadrilaterals in the puzzle.

1. Color one square red.

2. Color one parallelogram blue.

3. Color one rectangle green.

4. Color one trapezoid yellow.

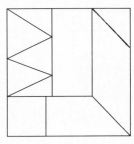

Complete the drawing of each quadrilateral.

5. Square

6. Trapezoid

7. Parallelogram

8. Rectangle

Addison-Wesley | All Rights Reserved

Congruent Figures

Figures that have the same size and shape are **congruent**.
Each pair of figures below is congruent.

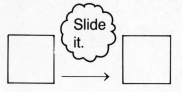

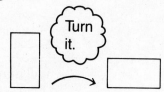

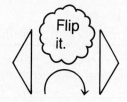

Use tracing paper to decide which figures are congruent.
Write **congruent** or **not congruent.** You may need to slide,
turn, or flip your tracing paper.

1. _____

2. _____

3. _____

Use tracing paper to draw congruent figures.

4.   **5.** 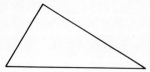   **6.**

Addison-Wesley | All Rights Reserved

Name _____

Curves and Circles

Here are 4 geometric figures made for curves.

Curves   **Circle**

simple closed	not closed	not simple

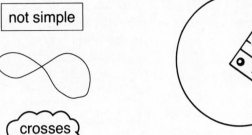

The ends are not connected.

crosses itself

Distance between the center and any point on the circle is always the same.

Write the name of the geometric figure shown.

1. _____

2. _____

3. ⬭ _____

4. _____

5.  _____

6. _____

Draw these.

7. Simple closed curve   **8.** Not simple curve   **9.** Not closed curve

---

Name _____

Coordinate Geometry

A pair of numbers describes the location of a point. The
numbers in the pair are called **coordinates.** Find the point
located by the coordinates (4, 3).

| Start at 0. | → | Go right as many units as the first number. | → | Go up as many units as the second number. |

Go right 4.   Go up 3.

```
6
5
4
3        ●
2
1
0  1  2  3  4  5  6
```

Mark the point.

Coordinates (4, 3)

Write the coordinates for the point that locates each object.

1. tree _____   **2.** flower _____

3. cat _____   **4.** dog _____

5. slide _____   **6.** seesaw _____

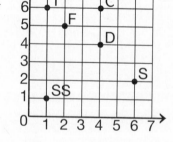

Graph these coordinates. Then connect them in order.

$(3, 2) \rightarrow (2, 3) \rightarrow (2, 4) \rightarrow (3, 5) \rightarrow$
$(4, 5) \rightarrow (5, 4) \rightarrow (5, 3) \rightarrow (4, 2) \rightarrow (3, 2)$

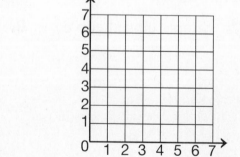

Addison-Wesley | All Rights Reserved

Name _____

Similar Figures

Two figures that have the same shape, but not necessarily the same size, are **similar** to each other.

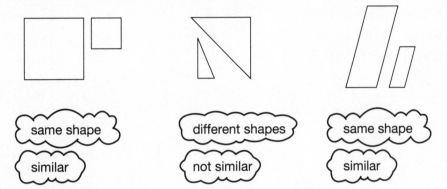

Ring the figure that is similar to the first.

1.

2.

3.

Use the graph paper. Draw a figure that is similar, that has the same shape, but not the same size as the model.

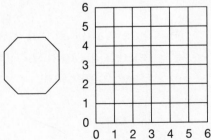

Addison-Wesley | All Rights Reserved

Name _____

Data from a Diagram

To solve some problems you must first locate the needed data in a diagram.

Here is a diagram that shows the floor plan for Nan's bedroom. What is the total length of the two longest walls?

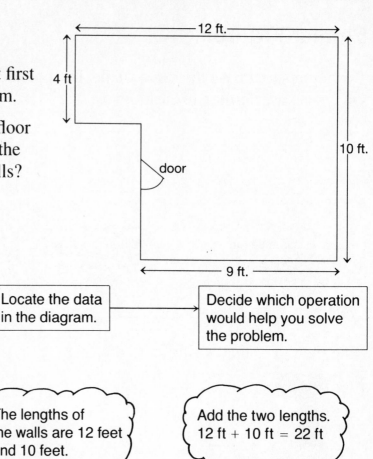

Read the question. Decide what data are needed.	→	Locate the data in the diagram.	→	Decide which operation would help you solve the problem.

I need to find out which two walls are the longest.

The lengths of the walls are 12 feet and 10 feet.

Add the two lengths.
12 ft + 10 ft = 22 ft

The total length of the two longest walls in Nan's bedroom is 22 ft.

Solve using the floor plan.

1. What is the length of the shortest wall? _____

2. What is the length of the wall with the door? _____

3. Nan's uncle is building a shelf the full length of the second longest wall for all Nan's stuffed animals.

How long will the shelf be? _____

4. Nan wants to put a wallpaper border around the top of the room. How many feet of wallpaper border is needed? _____

Understanding Fractions

What fraction of the flag is white?

5 pairs are white. $\longrightarrow$ **5**
Each part is a sixth. $\longrightarrow$ **6**

$\dfrac{5}{6}$ of the flag is white.

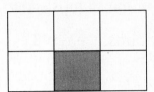

Ring the fraction that tells what part is white.

1.

3 parts are white. Each part is a fourth.

A $\dfrac{1}{4}$ **B** $\dfrac{1}{3}$ $\left(\textbf{C}\ \dfrac{3}{4}\right)$

2.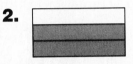

A $\dfrac{2}{3}$ **B** $\dfrac{1}{3}$ **C** $\dfrac{1}{2}$

3.

A $\dfrac{2}{3}$ **B** $\dfrac{3}{5}$ **C** $\dfrac{2}{5}$

4.

A $\dfrac{4}{10}$ **B** $\dfrac{4}{6}$ **C** $\dfrac{6}{10}$

5.

A $\dfrac{0}{8}$ **B** $\dfrac{8}{8}$ **C** $\dfrac{1}{8}$

6.

A $\dfrac{5}{9}$ **B** $\dfrac{4}{9}$ **C** $\dfrac{4}{5}$

Write a fraction to tell what part is shaded.

7.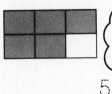

5 parts are shaded. Each part is a sixth.

$\dfrac{5}{6}$

8.

_____

9.

_____

10.

_____

11.

_____

12.

_____

More About Fractions

What fraction of the stamps shows birds?

3 stamps show birds. $\longrightarrow \dfrac{3}{8}$
8 stamps in all $\longrightarrow$

$\dfrac{3}{8}$ of the stamps show birds.

Write the fraction of each stamp set that shows birds.

1.

$\dfrac{5}{8}$ 5 bird stamps out of 8 stamps

_____

2.

_____

3.

_____

Write the fraction that makes each sentence true.

4.

1 of the 5 bowls has fish.

$\dfrac{1}{5}$ _____ of the bowls have fish.

5.

_____ of the bowls have fish.

6.

_____ of the bowls have fish.

7.

_____ of the set are soccer balls.

8.

_____ of the set are baseballs.

9.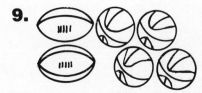

_____ of the set are footballs.

Estimating Fractional Parts

Think about these fractions to help you estimate fractional parts.

$\frac{1}{10}$ $\frac{1}{8}$ $\frac{1}{4}$ $\frac{1}{3}$ $\frac{1}{2}$ 1 whole

1. Is the shaded part more or less than $\frac{1}{3}$?

2. Is the shaded part more or less than $\frac{2}{4}$?

_____   _____

Ring the best fractional estimate for the shaded part of each figure.

3.

$\frac{2}{3}$ $\frac{1}{2}$ $\frac{7}{8}$

4.

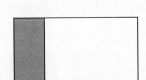

$\frac{2}{3}$ $\frac{1}{4}$ $\frac{9}{10}$

5.

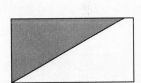

$\frac{1}{2}$ $\frac{1}{4}$ $\frac{1}{3}$

Draw some rectangles and estimate to color in these amounts.

6. $\frac{3}{10}$ **7.** $\frac{1}{5}$ **8.** $\frac{7}{8}$

Equivalent Fractions

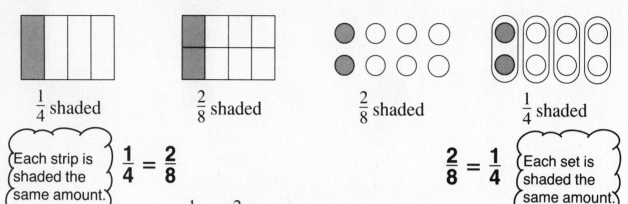

$\frac{1}{4}$ shaded $\frac{2}{8}$ shaded $\frac{2}{8}$ shaded $\frac{1}{4}$ shaded

(Each strip is shaded the same amount.) $\frac{1}{4} = \frac{2}{8}$ $\frac{2}{8} = \frac{1}{4}$ (Each set is shaded the same amount.)

$\frac{1}{4}$ and $\frac{2}{8}$ are **equivalent fractions**.
Fractions that name the same amount
are **equivalent** to each other.

Complete the equivalent fraction.

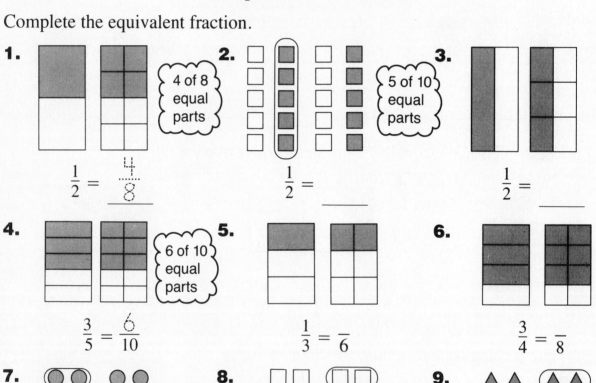

1. $\frac{1}{2} = \frac{4}{8}$

2. (4 of 8 equal parts) $\frac{1}{2} = $ _____

3. (5 of 10 equal parts) $\frac{1}{2} = $ _____

4. (6 of 10 equal parts) $\frac{3}{5} = \frac{6}{10}$

5. $\frac{1}{3} = \frac{}{6}$

6. $\frac{3}{4} = \frac{}{8}$

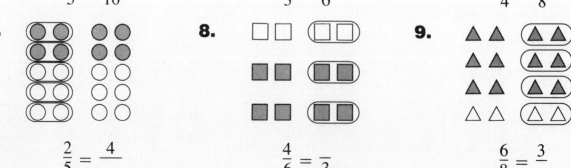

7. $\frac{2}{5} = \frac{4}{}$

8. $\frac{4}{6} = \frac{}{3}$

9. $\frac{6}{8} = \frac{3}{}$

More About Equivalent Fractions

You can find equivalent fractions by multiplying the
numerator and denominator by the same number.

 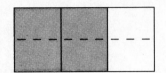

$$\frac{2}{3} = \frac{4}{6}$$

2 times as many shaded parts
2 times as many total parts

Color $\frac{3}{4}$ of each rectangle. Then complete the chart.

	Rectangle	Number of Colored Parts	Total Number of Parts	Fraction
1.				
2.				
3.				
4.				

Use your chart to find equivalent fractions. Write the number
by which you would multiply the numerator and denominator.

5. $\frac{3}{4} = \frac{}{8}$ ___   **6.** $\frac{3}{4} = \frac{}{12}$ ___   **7.** $\frac{3}{4} = \frac{}{16}$ ___

Now find these equivalent fractions.

8. $\frac{6}{8} =$ **9.** $\frac{4}{5} =$ **10.** $\frac{5}{6} =$

Lowest Terms Fractions

To reduce a fraction to lowest terms, use division
to find an equivalent fraction that cannot be reduced.

$\frac{8}{16}$ of the socks have stripes.

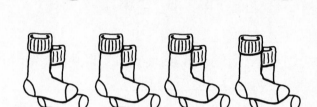

$\frac{8}{16} = \frac{4}{8} \rightarrow \frac{4}{8}$ of the pairs have stripes.

$\frac{4}{8} = \frac{1}{2} \rightarrow \frac{1}{2}$ of the socks have stripes.

Is the fraction in lowest terms? Ring **yes** or **no**.

1. $\frac{4}{6}$ yes (no) *I can still divide both 4 and 6 by 2.*

2. $\frac{2}{3}$ (yes) no *I cannot divide both 2 and 3 by the same number.*

3. $\frac{6}{8}$ yes no *I can still divide both 6 and 8 by 2.*

4. $\frac{8}{10}$ yes no

5. $\frac{3}{9}$ yes no

6. $\frac{3}{5}$ yes no

Reduce each fraction to lowest terms. Divide the numerator
and denominator by the same number.

7. ÷2 $\frac{6}{10} = \frac{3}{5}$

8. ÷2 $\frac{6}{8} = $ _____

9. ÷3 $\frac{6}{9} = $ _____

10. ÷6 $\frac{6}{12} = $ _____

11. ÷2 $\frac{8}{10} = $ _____

12. ÷2 $\frac{3}{12} = $ _____

13. ÷3 $\frac{5}{15} = $ _____

14. ÷6 $\frac{2}{6} = $ _____

Comparing Fractions

Which is larger, $\frac{1}{2}$ or $\frac{5}{8}$?

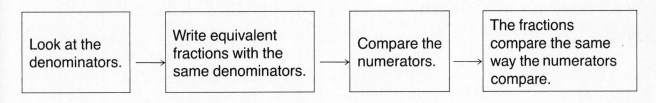

| Look at the denominators. | → | Write equivalent fractions with the same denominators. | → | Compare the numerators. | → | The fractions compare the same way the numerators compare. |

$\frac{1}{2}$ Not the same. $\frac{5}{8}$

$\frac{1}{2} = \frac{4}{8}$ Make both denominators 8. $\frac{5}{8} = \frac{5}{8}$

$\frac{4}{8}$ $5 > 4$ $\frac{5}{8}$

$\frac{5}{8} > \frac{4}{8}$

so $\frac{5}{8} > \frac{1}{2}$

Write the missing numerators. Then write $>$, $<$, or $=$ for each $\bigcirc$.

1. $\frac{2}{3} = \frac{8}{12}$
$\frac{3}{4} = \frac{9}{12}$
$8 < 9$
so $\frac{2}{3} \boxed{<} \frac{3}{4}$

2. $\frac{1}{3} = \frac{}{15}$
$\frac{2}{5} = \frac{}{15}$
so $\frac{1}{3} \bigcirc \frac{2}{5}$

3. $\frac{3}{4} = \frac{}{20}$
$\frac{2}{5} = \frac{}{20}$
so $\frac{3}{4} \bigcirc \frac{2}{5}$

Write the denominators. Then write $>$, $<$, or $=$ for each $\bigcirc$.

4. $\frac{1}{4} = \frac{5}{20}$
$\frac{2}{5} = \frac{8}{20}$
$5 < 8$
so $\frac{1}{4} \bigcirc \frac{2}{5}$

5. $\frac{2}{3} = \frac{8}{}$
$\frac{3}{4} = \frac{9}{}$
so $\frac{2}{3} \bigcirc \frac{3}{4}$

6. $\frac{2}{5} = \frac{8}{}$
$\frac{1}{4} = \frac{5}{}$
so $\frac{2}{5} \bigcirc \frac{1}{4}$

7. $\frac{2}{3} = \frac{10}{}$
$\frac{4}{5} = \frac{12}{}$
so $\frac{2}{3} \bigcirc \frac{4}{5}$

8. $\frac{4}{5} = \frac{16}{}$
$\frac{3}{4} = \frac{15}{}$
so $\frac{4}{5} \bigcirc \frac{3}{4}$

9. $\frac{5}{7} = \frac{20}{}$
$\frac{3}{4} = \frac{21}{}$
so $\frac{5}{7} \bigcirc \frac{3}{4}$

Name _____

Exploring Algebra

You can graph fractions. Use the numerator and denominator as the ordered pair. $\frac{1}{3}$ can be written (1, 3).

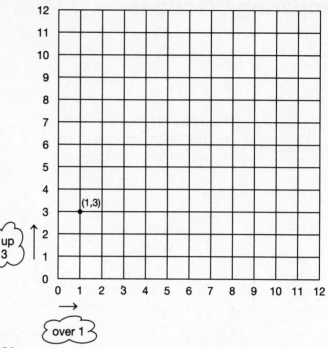

1. Complete the table below. Replace △ and □ with numbers to make fractions equivalent to $\frac{1}{3}$.

$$\frac{1}{3} = \frac{\triangle}{\square}$$

△	1	2		
□	3	6		

2. Write the pairs of numbers as an ordered pair. Use the order (△, □).

$\frac{1}{3} \rightarrow$ (1, 3)

$\frac{2}{6} \rightarrow$ _____

_____   _____

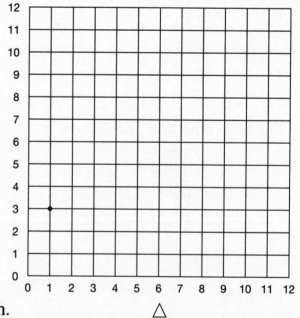

3. Graph the ordered pairs on the graph.

4. Connect the points on the graph. What do you notice?

_____

Finding a Fraction of a Number

9 walnuts

How many in $\frac{1}{3}$?

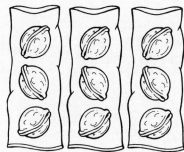

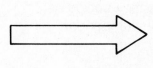

$\frac{1}{3}$ of 9 = 3

To find $\frac{1}{3}$ of a number, divide by 3.

Find the missing number.

1.
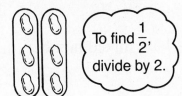
To find $\frac{1}{2}$, divide by 2.

$\frac{1}{2}$ of 6 = ___3___

2.
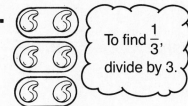
To find $\frac{1}{3}$, divide by 3.

$\frac{1}{3}$ of 6 = _____

3.
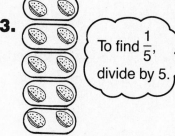
To find $\frac{1}{5}$, divide by 5.

$\frac{1}{5}$ of 10 = _____

4.
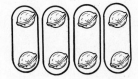

$\frac{1}{4}$ of 8 = _____

5.
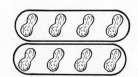

$\frac{1}{2}$ of 8 = _____

6.
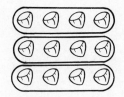

$\frac{1}{3}$ of 12 = _____

Divide by 3.

7. $\frac{1}{3}$ of 15 = _____

8. $\frac{1}{2}$ of 4 = _____

9. $\frac{1}{3}$ of 6 = _____

10. $\frac{1}{2}$ of 10 = _____

11. $\frac{1}{5}$ of 15 = _____

12. $\frac{1}{4}$ of 16 = _____

13. $\frac{1}{2}$ of 14 = _____

14. $\frac{1}{3}$ of 12 = _____

15. $\frac{1}{2}$ of 10 = _____

Mixed Numbers

Use division to write a mixed number for a fraction greater than 1.

| Divide the numerator by the denominator. | → | Write the quotient as the whole number part. | → | Write the remainder over the divisor as the fraction part. |

$$\frac{7}{2} \rightarrow 2\overline{)7} \begin{array}{c} 3 \leftarrow \text{wholes} \\ -6 \\ \hline 1 \leftarrow \text{halves} \end{array}$$

3 quotient

$3\frac{1}{2}$ 1 is remainder.

2 is divisor.

Divide. Then write as a mixed number.

1. $\frac{7}{3} \rightarrow 3\overline{)7} \begin{array}{c} 2 \\ -6 \\ \hline 1 \end{array}$ mixed number $2\frac{1}{3}$

2. $\frac{9}{4} \rightarrow 4\overline{)9}$ mixed number _____

Divide 15 by 4.

3. $\frac{13}{3} \rightarrow 3\overline{)}$ mixed number _____

4. $\frac{15}{4} \rightarrow \overline{)}$ mixed number _____

5. $\frac{19}{2} \rightarrow \overline{)}$ mixed number _____

6. $\frac{19}{6} \rightarrow \overline{)}$ mixed number _____

Write as a whole number or a mixed number.

7. $\frac{13}{4} = 3\frac{1}{4}$

8. $\frac{37}{4} =$ _____

9. $\frac{6}{6} =$ _____

10. $\frac{32}{4} =$ _____

Measuring to a Fractional Part of an Inch

This ruler is divided into quarter and half inches. The longest lines show **inch** markings. The shorter lines show **half-inch** markings. The shortest lines show **quarter-inch** markings.

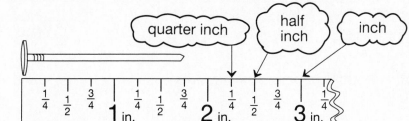

The length of this nail is between 1 and 2 inches. It is on the $\frac{3}{4}$ inch mark. The length of this nail is $1\frac{3}{4}$ inches.

Use your ruler to find each length.

1.

_____

2.

_____

3.

_____

4.

_____

Find the length of each nail to the nearest quarter inch.

5.

_____

6.

_____

7.

_____

8.

_____

Reading and Writing Decimals: Tenths

A fraction or a mixed number that uses tenths can easily be
written as a decimal.

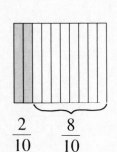

	Say	**Write**	
		fraction	decimal
	shaded part: "two tenths"	$\frac{2}{10}$	0.2
	white part: "eight tenths"	$\frac{8}{10}$	0.8

$\frac{2}{10}$ $\frac{8}{10}$

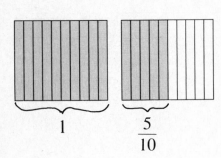

	mixed number	decimal
	$1\frac{5}{10}$	1.5

1        $\frac{5}{10}$

Write the fraction and the decimal to tell how much
is shaded.

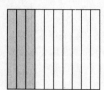   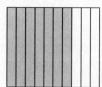   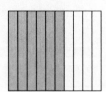

1. _____   **2.** _____   **3.** _____

Write a decimal for the amount.

4. one and four tenths _____   **5.** two and three tenths _____

6. sixteen and two tenths _____   **7.** eleven and five tenths _____

Reading and Writing Decimals: Hundredths

Show	**Say**	**Write**

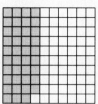

"thirty-nine hundredths"   0.39

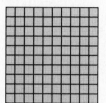

Say "one and six tenths" or "one and sixty hundredths"

mixed number

$1\frac{6}{10}$ or $1\frac{60}{100}$

decimal

1.6 or 1.60

Write a fraction or mixed number and a decimal to tell how much is shaded.

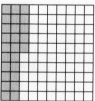

1. _____

2. _____

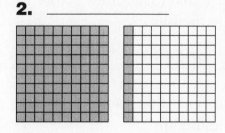

3. _____

4. _____

Write a decimal for each.

5. two and six hundredths _____

6. fifty-nine hundredths _____

7. four and one hundredth _____

8. thirty-three hundredths _____

Decimals: Counting and Order

You can use a calculator to help you count and order by tenths and hundredths. When counting by tenths, what decimals come next?

14.7, 14.8, _____ , _____ , _____

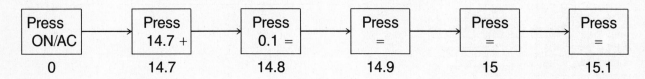

Press ON/AC	Press 14.7 +	Press 0.1 =	Press =	Press =	Press =
0	14.7	14.8	14.9	15	15.1

14.9, 15.0, 15.1 come next.

When counting by hundreths, press **0.01** instead of **0.1.**

Give the next four decimals in the counting pattern.

1. 15.2   15.3   15.4   15.5   15.6   _____ _____ _____ _____

2. 1.52   1.53   1.54   1.55   1.56   _____ _____ _____ _____

Write the decimal that comes before each number when you count by hundredths.

3. _____ , 1.53   **4.** _____ , 1.47   **5.** _____ , 1.71

Write the decimal that comes after each number when you count by hundredths.

6. 1.85, _____   **7.** 1.26, _____   **8.** 15.12, _____

Write the decimal that comes between each pair of numbers when you count by hundredths.

9. 1.55, _____ , 1.57   **10.** 4.50, _____ , 4.52

Comparing and Ordering Decimals

Which number is larger, 6.9 or 6.4? Here is a way to
compare decimals.

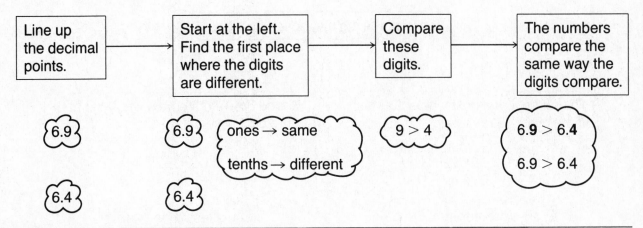

| Line up the decimal points. | → | Start at the left. Find the first place where the digits are different. | → | Compare these digits. | → | The numbers compare the same way the digits compare. |

6.9   6.9   ones → same   9 > 4   6.9 > 6.4

6.4   6.4   tenths → different   6.9 > 6.4

Write >, <, or = for each ◯.

1. 6.7 ◯ 4.8   **2.** 21.5 ◯ 21.9   **3.** 4.76 ◯ 4.67

Write whether each equation is true or false. If it is false,
write <, >, or = to make it true.

4. 3.45 < 3.54 _____   **5.** 6.54 < 6.65 _____

6. 0.43 = 4.03 _____   **7.** 8.8 > 8.79 _____

Use the numbers in the box to answer these questions.

| 6.5 | 4.3 |
| 2.1 | 7.21 |

8. Write the numbers greater than 4.9. _____

9. Write the numbers less than 2.34. _____

10. Write the numbers between 6.44 and 7.61. _____

11. Order the numbers from least to greatest. _____

Rounding Decimals

Here is how you can round a decimal to the nearest whole number.

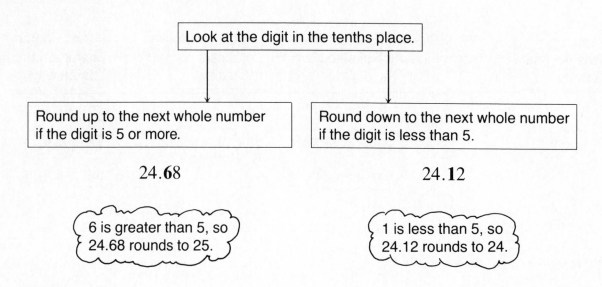

Look at the digit in the tenths place.

Round up to the next whole number if the digit is 5 or more.

Round down to the next whole number if the digit is less than 5.

24.**68**

24.**12**

6 is greater than 5, so 24.68 rounds to 25.

1 is less than 5, so 24.12 rounds to 24.

You can use a number line to be sure you have rounded correctly.

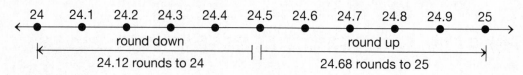

24   24.1   24.2   24.3   24.4   24.5   24.6   24.7   24.8   24.9   25

round down

24.12 rounds to 24

round up

24.68 rounds to 25

Round each decimal to the nearest whole number. Use the number line to check your answer.

1. 24.11 _____   **2.** 24.86 _____   **3.** 24.01 _____   **4.** 24.98 _____

Round each decimal to the nearest whole number.

5. 4.6 _____   **6.** 7.2 _____   **7.** 0.7 _____

8. 5.1 _____   **9.** 14.3 _____   **10.** 24.9 _____

11. 7.38 _____   **12.** 4.79 _____   **13.** 20.75 _____

14. 15.66 _____   **15.** 34.34 _____   **16.** 61.29 _____

Decimals and Fractions

You can use graph paper to find the decimal for $\frac{3}{5}$.

| Use a 10 × 10 square. | → | Color the square to show the fraction. | → | Count the hundredths. |

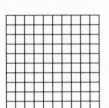

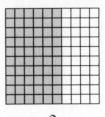

$\frac{3}{5}$

60 hundredths = 0.60

You can also use a calculator to find the decimal for $\frac{3}{5}$.

$\boxed{\text{AC/ON}}$ 3 $\boxed{\div}$ 5 $\boxed{=}$ 0.60

Count small squares and write a decimal for each fraction.

1.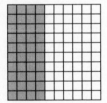

2.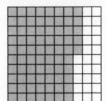

3.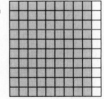

_____   _____   _____

Use your calculator to find a decimal for these fractions.

4. $\frac{4}{5}$ _____

5. $\frac{2}{4}$ _____

6. $\frac{2}{8}$ _____

7. $\frac{6}{10}$ _____

8. $\frac{1}{5}$ _____

9. $\frac{8}{10}$ _____

10. $\frac{3}{4}$ _____

11. $\frac{3}{15}$ _____

12. $\frac{3}{10}$ _____

Addison-Wesley | All Rights Reserved

Determining Reasonable Answers

Always check your work to see if your answers are reasonable. Use estimation.

Theo found a desk for $65.98 at one store and the same type of desk at another store for $84.25. What is the difference in the prices?

Theo's answer: | 8.24 | .

Is his answer reasonable?

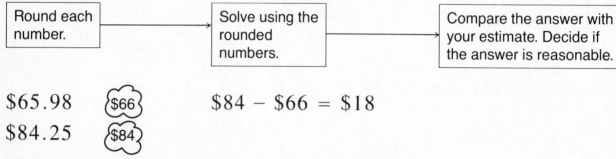

| Round each number. | → | Solve using the rounded numbers. | → | Compare the answer with your estimate. Decide if the answer is reasonable. |

$65.98   ($66) $84 − $66 = $18

$84.25   ($84)

His answer does not seem reasonable. $8.24 is too low.

Do not solve the problems. Decide if the answers are reasonable. If an answer is not reasonable, explain why.

1. Maria put a bookshelf in her room. She has 144 books to be placed on 6 shelves. If she puts the same number of books on each shelf, how many books will be on each shelf? Maria's answer: | 30. | .

2. Theresa ordered new tennis racquets for her team. Each racquet costs $8.95. How much would 12 racquets cost? Theresa's answer: | 107.40 | .

3. Trevor ordered shirts for 8 team members. The bill came to $47.60. How much should each team member pay? Trevor's answer: | 5.95 | .

4. Leila's team had a book fair. There were 275 bags of books sold. Each bag sold for a quarter. How much money did the team raise? Leila's answer: | 45.50 | .

Name _____

Centimeters, Decimeters, Meters, and Kilometers

Centimeter, decimeter, meter, and **kilometer** are metric units of length. The approximate length of four everyday objects is shown below.

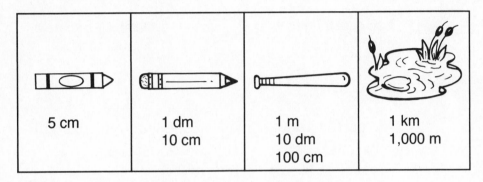

| 5 cm | 1 dm
10 cm | 1 m
10 dm
100 cm | 1 km
1,000 m |

Which is longer: a pool (400 dm) or a tree (10 m)?

To compare, change meters to decimeters: Multiply the number of meters by 10. → Pool is 400 dm.
Tree is 100 dm.   Pool is longer.

Ring the longer measurement.

1. 1 dm   **2.** 5 km   **3.** 400 cm   **4.** 52 dm
   12 cm   600 m   3 m   4 m

Ring the object that is taller.

5. Flagpole
   Ladder

90 dm

6. Man
   Door

7. Ladder
   Door

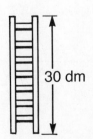

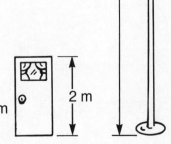

30 dm

190 cm

2 m

Addison-Wesley | All Rights Reserved

Estimating Length: Unitizing

Use unitizing to estimate the length of this object.

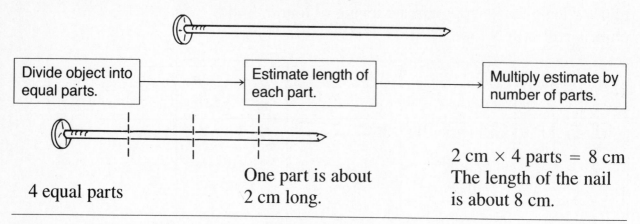

| Divide object into equal parts. | → | Estimate length of each part. | → | Multiply estimate by number of parts. |

4 equal parts

One part is about 2 cm long.

2 cm × 4 parts = 8 cm
The length of the nail is about 8 cm.

Use unitizing to estimate each length in centimeters. Then measure the length to the nearest centimeter. Find the difference between the estimated and actual measures.

Record your data in the table below.

Estimates and differences may vary.

	Object	Estimate	Measure	Difference
1.	screwdriver			
2.	pencil			
3.	hammer			
4.	screw			

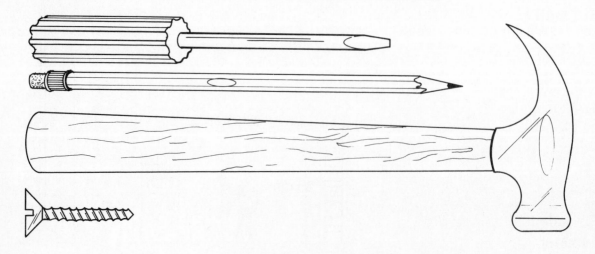

Millimeters

A **millimeter** is a very small metric unit of length.

$$1 \text{ cm} = 10 \text{ mm}$$

Find the height of this bottle in millimeters.

| Find the length in centimeters and extra millimeters. | → | Use mental math to change **cm** to **mm** and add the extra millimeters. |

$5 \times 10 \text{ mm} = 50 \text{ mm}$

$5 \text{ cm} + 2 \text{ mm} = 52 \text{ mm}$

The bottle is 52 mm.

Use a millimeter ruler to write the height of the corn plant for each week.

1.

first week: _____

2.

second week: _____

3.

third week: _____

4.

fourth week: _____

Addison-Wesley | All Rights Reserved

Name _____

Deciding When to Estimate

Sometimes to solve a problem, you can estimate a
measurement. Other times an exact measure is needed.

Only an estimate is needed	**Actual measure is needed**
▶ when you need to know only "about what is the measure."	▶ when exact measurement is necessary to solve the problem.
▶ when comparing with a reference point.	

Decide whether an estimate or an actual measure is needed.
Tell why.

1. Judy is making a dress for the school play. She needs to add trim around the neck. How much trim does she need?

- Will an estimate work? _____
- Does she need the actual measure? _____
- Why? _____
_____

2. Pedro is in charge of the props for the play. He must put the tree on the stage after Act I. How far from the edge of the stage should the tree be placed?

_____
_____

3. Vanessa will provide the refreshments during intermission. How much punch should she make for 150 people?

_____
_____

4. Bill needs to make a door for the hut in the play. What size plywood should he buy?

_____
_____

5. Jerry is meeting friends after the play. At what time should he tell his friends the play will be over?

_____
_____

Addison-Wesley | All Rights Reserved

Area

The **square centimeter** is a metric unit for measuring **area.** You can use multiplication to find the area of rectangular regions.

 2 rows

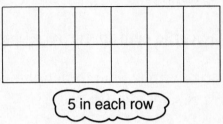

5 in each row

2 rows × 5 in each row

2 × 5 = 10 square centimeters

Write the area of each region in square centimeters. Use multiplication when you can.

1.

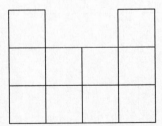

2 rows

6 in each row

____2____ rows × ____6____ in each row = ___12___ square centimeters

2.

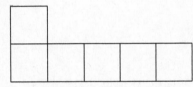

_____

3.

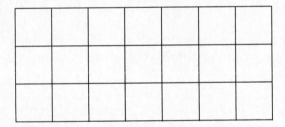

_____ rows × _____ in each row =

_____ square centimeters.

4.

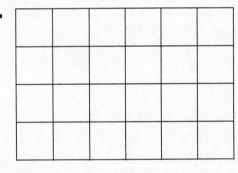

_____

5.

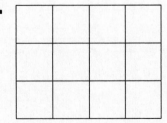

_____

6.

_____

Addison-Wesley | All Rights Reserved

Volume

The **cubic centimeter** is a meter unit for measuring **volume**.

Use multiplication to find the volume
of a rectangular prism.

| Rows × number in each row × layers |

$$1 \quad \times \quad 4 \quad \times \quad 2 = 8$$

The volume is 8 cubic centimeters.

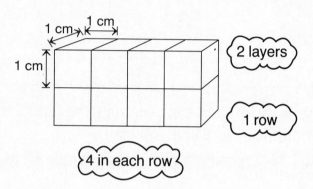

Write the volume of each figure in cubic centimeters.

1.

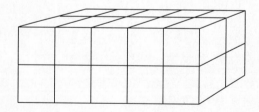

1 layer
3 rows

7 in each row

_____

2.

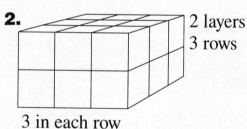

2 layers
3 rows

3 in each row

_____

3.

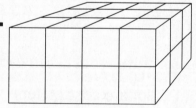

_____

4.

_____

5.

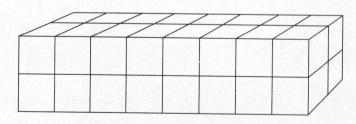

_____

Finding Related Problems

Many problems are related. These problems can be solved using the same strategy. Sometimes it helps if you can think about a related problem. At the right are a list of strategies to choose from to solve the following problems.

Some Strategies
Choose an Operation
Draw a Picture
Guess and Check
Make a Table
Work Backward

Solve. Then answer the strategy questions to help you understand how the pairs of problems are related.

1. Roberta took a spelling test. There were 25 problems on the test. She got 15 more right answers than wrong answers. How many answers did Roberta get right?

_____

2. Jonathan spent $14 for two tapes. One tape cost $2 more than the other. How much did the higher-priced tape cost?

_____

What strategy did you use to solve both problems?

_____

3. Each coat the tailor makes takes 4 buttons and 2 shoulder pads. When the tailor has used 12 buttons, how many shoulder pads will he have used?

_____

4. Mr. Kim gives clarinet lessons to 5 boys and 6 girls a week. When he has taught 20 boys, how many girls has he taught?

_____

What strategy did you use to solve both problems?

_____

5. There were 15 crew members for two flights. The early flight had 3 more members than the late flight. How many crew members were on the first flight?

_____

Is this problem related to Problem 2 or Problem 4? _____

Addison-Wesley | All Rights Reserved

Capacity

Liter and **milliliter** are metric units for measuring **capacity.**

1 mL

1 L = 1,000 mL

Which unit would you use for measuring the capacity of this can?

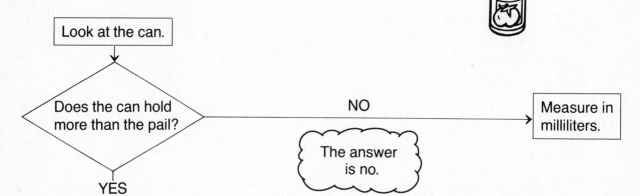

| Look at the can. |

Does the can hold more than the pail?

NO → Measure in milliliters.

The answer is no.

YES ↓

Measure in liters.

You would use milliliters to measure the can's capacity.

Write which unit, **liter** or **milliliter,** you would use for measuring the capacity.

1.    **2.**   **3.**

_____   _____   _____

Ring the better estimate of capacity.

4.

more than 100 mL
less than or equal to 100 mL

5.

more than 1 L
less than or equal to 1 L

Grams and Kilograms/Temperature: Degrees Celsius

Mass

Gram (g) and **kilogram** (kg) are metric units of **mass.**

1 kg = 1,000 g

A nickel weighs about 5 g.

This bat weighs about 1 kg.

You can use benchmarks like these to help you estimate the mass of objects.

Ring the best mass for each item.

1.

   A 1g   **B** 1 kg   **C** 10 g

2.

   A 16 g   **B** 16 kg   **C** 3 kg

Estimate whether the mass of each object is nearer 5 g or 1 kg.

3. _____

5.  _____

6. _____

Temperature
Degrees Celsius (°C)

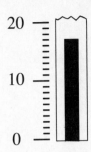

The temperature is 17°C to the nearest degree.

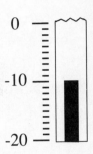

−10°C is below 0°C. We read this temperature as "negative 10 degrees" or "10 degrees below zero."

Record each temperature shown.

7.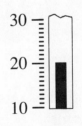

8.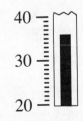

_____   _____

9.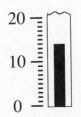

10.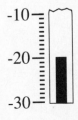

_____   _____

Addison-Wesley | All Rights Reserved

Name _____

Adding and Subtracting Fractions with Like Denominators: Making the Connection

Use fraction pieces for fourths.

Addition $\frac{1}{4} + \frac{2}{4} = ?$

 + =

$\frac{1}{4}$ + $\frac{2}{4}$ = $\frac{3}{4}$

Cover 1 section.　　　Cover 2 more sections.　　　3 sections are covered.

Subtraction $\frac{3}{4} - \frac{2}{4} = ?$

 − 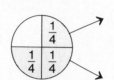 =

$\frac{3}{4}$ − $\frac{2}{4}$ = $\frac{1}{4}$

Cover 3 sections.　　　Take away 2 sections.　　　1 section left covered.

Use fraction pieces to find the sums and differences. Reduce your answers to lowest terms.

1. + =

$\frac{1}{6}$ + $\frac{4}{6}$ = _____

2. − =

$\frac{7}{8}$ − $\frac{3}{8}$ = _____

3. $\frac{2}{5} + \frac{1}{5} =$ _____

4. $\frac{6}{7} - \frac{4}{7} =$ _____

5. $\frac{2}{6} + \frac{2}{6} =$ _____

6. $\frac{2}{3} - \frac{1}{3} =$ _____

7. $\frac{1}{4} + \frac{1}{4} =$ _____

8. $\frac{4}{5} - \frac{2}{5} =$ _____

Name _____

Adding and Subtracting Fractions: Like Denominators

Look at the denominators.	→	Add or subtract the numerators.	→	Write the sum or difference over the denominator. Simplify.

$\frac{8}{9} + \frac{5}{9}$ The denominators are alike.

$8 + 5 = 13$

$\frac{8}{9} + \frac{5}{9} = \frac{13}{9} = 1\frac{4}{9}$

$\frac{3}{4} - \frac{1}{4}$

$3 - 1 = 2$

$\frac{3}{4} - \frac{1}{4} = \frac{2}{4} = \frac{1}{2}$

To add mixed numbers

$4\frac{2}{8} + 3\frac{1}{8} = ?$

First add the whole numbers. $4 + 3 = 7$
Then add the fractions. $\frac{2}{8} + \frac{1}{8} = \frac{3}{8}$

$4\frac{2}{8} + 3\frac{1}{8} = 7\frac{3}{8}$

Find these sums and differences. Simplify.

1. $\frac{2}{5}$ (2+1) $+ \frac{1}{5}$

2. $\frac{5}{7}$ (5−2) $- \frac{2}{7}$

3. $\frac{7}{8}$ $- \frac{5}{8}$

4. $\frac{1}{6}$ $+ \frac{3}{6}$

5. $1\frac{2}{10}$ $+ 4\frac{5}{10}$

6. $2\frac{1}{8}$ $+ 1\frac{5}{8}$

7. $5\frac{5}{6}$ $- 3\frac{4}{6}$

8. $3\frac{8}{10}$ $- 2\frac{3}{10}$

9. $\frac{4}{5} + \frac{2}{5} =$ _____

10. $1\frac{2}{3} + 3\frac{1}{3} =$ _____

11. $\frac{5}{6} - \frac{2}{6} =$ _____

12. Add $\frac{4}{9}$ and $\frac{7}{9}$. _____

13. Find the difference of $\frac{6}{7}$ and $\frac{2}{7}$. _____

RS-4 Use with text pages 408-409. **147**

Data from a Recipe

Clair is making carrot bread and cranberry muffins for her
4-H bake sale.

Carrot Bread
$2\frac{1}{2}$ cups flour
1 cup sugar
$3\frac{1}{2}$ teaspoons baking powder
1 teaspoon salt
3 tablespoons salad oil
$\frac{3}{4}$ cup milk
1 egg
1 cup grated carrots

Cranberry Muffins
1 egg
$\frac{1}{2}$ cup milk
4 tablespoons salad oil
$1\frac{1}{2}$ cups flour
$\frac{3}{4}$ cup sugar
2 teaspoons baking powder
$\frac{1}{2}$ teaspoon salt
1 cup cranberries

Use the data from these recipes to answer the following
questions.

1. How much milk does Clair need for
both recipes?

▶ Milk for bread: ___$\frac{3}{4}$ cup___

▶ Milk for muffins: ___$\frac{1}{2}$ cup___

▶ Total needed: ___$\frac{3}{4} + \frac{1}{2} =$___

2. How much more flour is in the
bread than the muffins? _____

3. How much baking powder would
Clair need if she doubled both
recipes?

_____

4. How much sugar would Clair need
if she doubled both recipes?

_____

5. 3 carrots are used to make 1 cup of
grated carrots. How many carrots
are needed to make 4 cups of
grated carrots?

_____

Addison-Wesley | All Rights Reserved

Adding Fractions with Models: Unlike Denominators

$$\frac{1}{4} + \frac{1}{2} = ?$$

Cover the sections of the whole for each fraction.	→	Trade pieces to cover the same sections $\frac{1}{2}$ for $\frac{2}{4}$.	→	Find how many same-size pieces in all. Simplify if possible.

$$\frac{1}{4} \quad + \quad \frac{1}{2} \quad = \quad \frac{1}{4} + \frac{1}{2} \quad = \quad \frac{1}{4} + \frac{2}{4} \quad = \quad \frac{3}{4}.$$

Use fraction pieces to find each sum.

1.

$$\frac{1}{6} \quad + \quad \frac{2}{3} \quad = \quad \frac{1}{6} + \frac{2}{3} \quad = \quad \frac{1}{6} + \frac{}{6} \quad = \quad \frac{}{6}$$

2.

$$\frac{3}{8} \quad + \quad \frac{1}{4} \quad = \quad \frac{3}{8} + \frac{1}{4} \quad = \quad \frac{3}{8} + \underline{} \quad = \quad \underline{}$$

3. $\frac{1}{8} + \frac{1}{4} = $ _____

4. $\frac{3}{8} + \frac{1}{2} = $ _____

5. $\frac{1}{2} + \frac{2}{4} = $ _____

6. $\frac{1}{3} + \frac{3}{6} = $ _____

7. $\frac{1}{4} + \frac{3}{8} = $ _____

8. $\frac{1}{3} + \frac{1}{6} = $ _____

9. $\frac{2}{4} + \frac{3}{8} = $ _____

10. $\frac{4}{6} + \frac{1}{3} = $ _____

11. $\frac{4}{8} + \frac{1}{4} = $ _____

Subtracting Fractions with Models: Unlike Denominators

Subtract. $\dfrac{2}{3} - \dfrac{1}{6} = ?$

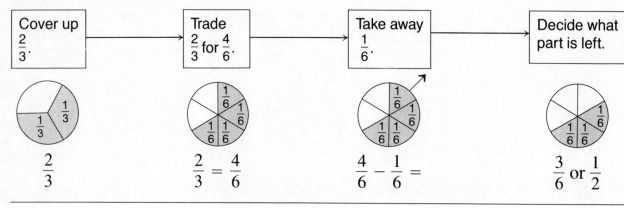

| Cover up $\dfrac{2}{3}$. | Trade $\dfrac{2}{3}$ for $\dfrac{4}{6}$. | Take away $\dfrac{1}{6}$. | Decide what part is left. |

$\dfrac{2}{3}$

$\dfrac{2}{3} = \dfrac{4}{6}$

$\dfrac{4}{6} - \dfrac{1}{6} =$

$\dfrac{3}{6}$ or $\dfrac{1}{2}$

Use fraction pieces to find each difference.

1. $\dfrac{1}{2} - \dfrac{1}{4}$

$\dfrac{1}{2}$

$\dfrac{1}{2} = \dfrac{}{4}$

$\dfrac{2}{4} - \dfrac{1}{4} = \dfrac{}{4}$

$\dfrac{1}{2} - \dfrac{1}{4} = $ _____

2. $\dfrac{5}{8} - \dfrac{1}{2}$

$\dfrac{5}{8}$

$\dfrac{1}{2} = \dfrac{}{8}$

$\dfrac{5}{8} - \dfrac{}{8} = \dfrac{}{8}$

$\dfrac{5}{8} - \dfrac{1}{2} = $ _____

This time we renamed the we took away.

3. $\dfrac{1}{3} - \dfrac{1}{6} = $ _____

4. $\dfrac{7}{8} - \dfrac{1}{2} = $ _____

5. $\dfrac{2}{3} - \dfrac{1}{6} = $ _____

6. $\dfrac{5}{6} - \dfrac{1}{3} = $ _____

7. $\dfrac{7}{8} - \dfrac{1}{4} = $ _____

8. $\dfrac{1}{3} - \dfrac{2}{6} = $ _____

9. $\dfrac{1}{2} - \dfrac{1}{6} = $ _____

10. $\dfrac{3}{4} - \dfrac{3}{8} = $ _____

11. $\dfrac{5}{6} - \dfrac{1}{2} = $ _____

Addison-Wesley | All Rights Reserved

Name _____

Exploring Algebra

Patterns can be represented by objects or drawing pictures.
A chart can be used to organize the data.

1st   2nd   3rd

N stands for the number of the Vs.
D stands for the number of dots needed for each V.

N	1	2	3	4	5
D	3	5	7		

As the number of the V increases by 1, the number of dots
increases by 2.

Look for a pattern. Fill in the blanks.

1st   2nd   3rd   4th

1. The first uses __5__ dots.   **2.** The second uses _____ dots.

3. The third uses _____ dots.   **4.** Complete the chart using these data.

N	1	2			
D	5				

5. Draw the next X design in the box.

6. How does the number of the X relate to the number of

dots needed? _____ _____ .

_____

7. What would *D* be when *N* is 9? _____

Addison-Wesley | All Rights Reserved

Name _____

Adding and Subtracting Decimals
Making the Connection

Addition

  1.65
+ 1.48
─────

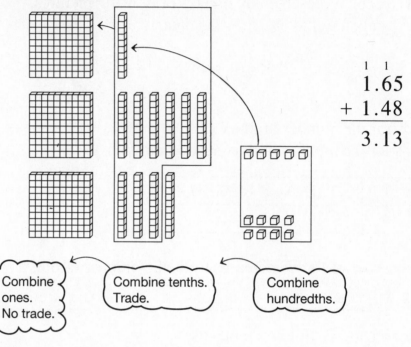

  ¹ ¹
  1.65
+ 1.48
─────
  3.13

Combine ones. No trade.

Combine tenths. Trade.

Combine hundredths.

Subtraction

4.42

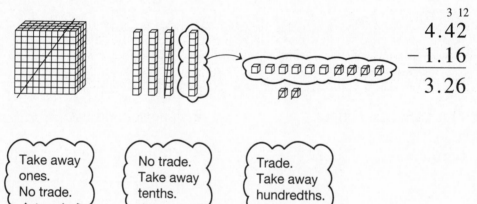

  ³ ¹²
  4.42
− 1.16
─────
  3.26

Take away ones. No trade.

No trade. Take away tenths.

Trade. Take away hundredths.

Use blocks to find these sums or differences.

1. $4.5 + 3.6 =$ _____   **2.** $1.36 + 4.26 =$ _____   **3.** $1.74 + 1.48 =$ _____

4. $6.2 - 4.7 =$ _____   **5.** $4.52 - 1.28 =$ _____   **6.** $6.34 - 2.61 =$ _____

7. $3.54 + 2.62 =$ _____   **8.** $5.81 - 3.54 -$ _____   **9.** $7.35 - 4.84 =$ _____

10. $2.98 + 6.34 =$ _____   **11.** $9.45 - 3.87 =$ _____   **12.** $2.59 + 3.87 =$ _____

Adding and Subtracting Decimals

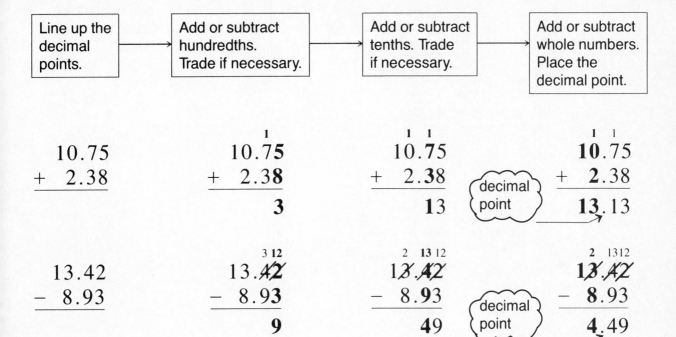

| Line up the decimal points. | → | Add or subtract hundredths. Trade if necessary. | → | Add or subtract tenths. Trade if necessary. | → | Add or subtract whole numbers. Place the decimal point. |

Add or subtract.

1.
```
  56.3
+ 14.5
------
 70.8
```

2.
```
  43.8
+ 38.2
------
 82.0
```

3.
```
 $13.13
- $ 6.27
-------
 $6.86
```

4.
```
  0.84
- 0.49
------
 0.35
```

5.
```
 19.47
-  7.09
------
 12.38
```

6.
```
  31.50
- 14.90
------
 16.60
```

7.
```
 $64.72
+ $38.26
-------
$102.98
```

8.
```
  40.28
+ 24.95
------
 65.23
```

9.
```
  57.04
-  8.16
------
 48.88
```

10.
```
  85.49
- 26.95
------
 58.54
```

Line up the decimal points. Then add or subtract.

11. 0.64 + 0.69
```
  0.64
+ 0.69
------
  1.33
```

12. $4.09 - $0.79
```
  $4.09
- $0.79
------
  $3.30
```

13. 48.06 + 3.41
```
  48.06
+  3.41
------
  51.47
```

More Adding and Subtracting Decimals

Line up the decimal points.	→	Annex a zero to show both decimal parts as hundredths.	→	Add or subtract. Place the decimal point.

$$\begin{array}{r} 13.4 \\ +\ \ 2.78 \\ \hline \end{array}$$

13.4 is the same as 13.40.

$$\begin{array}{r} 13.4\mathbf{0} \\ +\ \ 2.78 \\ \hline \end{array}$$

$$\begin{array}{r} \overset{1}{13.40} \\ +\ \ 2.78 \\ \hline 16.18 \end{array}$$

$$\begin{array}{r} 23.28 \\ -12.3 \\ \hline \end{array}$$

12.3 is the same as 12.30.

$$\begin{array}{r} 23.28 \\ -12.3\mathbf{0} \\ \hline \end{array}$$

$$\begin{array}{r} \overset{2\ \ 12}{2\cancel{3}.\cancel{2}8} \\ -12.30 \\ \hline 10.98 \end{array}$$

Find the sums and differences. Annex zeros when you need them.

1.
$$\begin{array}{r} 17.6 \\ +\ \ 2.45 \\ \hline \end{array}$$

2.
$$\begin{array}{r} 25.26 \\ -11.4 \\ \hline \end{array}$$

3.
$$\begin{array}{r} 6.42 \\ +\ 5. \\ \hline \end{array}$$

4.
$$\begin{array}{r} 17.6 \\ +\ \ 4.38 \\ \hline \end{array}$$

5.
$$\begin{array}{r} 52.6 \\ -\ 34 \\ \hline \end{array}$$

6.
$$\begin{array}{r} 67 \\ -\ 23.4 \\ \hline \end{array}$$

7.
$$\begin{array}{r} 30.08 \\ +\ \ 2.4 \\ \hline \end{array}$$

8.
$$\begin{array}{r} 28.7 \\ -\ 12.76 \\ \hline \end{array}$$

9.
$$\begin{array}{r} 38.4 \\ +\ \ 7.65 \\ \hline \end{array}$$

10.
$$\begin{array}{r} 68.4 \\ -\ 12.36 \\ \hline \end{array}$$

11.
$$\begin{array}{r} 3.78 \\ +\ 2. \\ \hline \end{array}$$

12.
$$\begin{array}{r} 85 \\ -\ 12.6 \\ \hline \end{array}$$

13. $36.3 + 8.51$

14. $40.08 + 0.6$

15. $68 - 24.25$

Estimating Decimal Sums and Differences

A | Round up. | → | Round each number up to next whole number. | → | Estimate the difference. |

$$\begin{array}{r} 6.7 \\ -\ 4.2 \\ \hline \end{array}$$
6.7 rounds up to 7
4.2 rounds up to 5
$$\begin{array}{r} 7 \\ -\ 5 \\ \hline 2 \end{array}$$

B | Round down. | → | Round each number down to next whole. | → | Estimate the sum. |

$$\begin{array}{r} 4.7 \\ +\ 3.4 \\ \hline \end{array}$$
4.7 rounds down to 4
3.4 rounds down to 3
$$\begin{array}{r} 4 \\ +\ 3 \\ \hline 7 \end{array}$$

C | Round to the nearest whole number. |
$$\begin{array}{r} 5.6 \rightarrow \quad 6 \\ +\ 4.3 \quad +\ 4 \\ \hline 10 \end{array}$$

Round down. Then estimate the sum.

1. $\begin{array}{r} 7.4 \\ +\ 2.1 \\ \hline \end{array}$
2. $\begin{array}{r} 10.13 \\ +\ 6.42 \\ \hline \end{array}$
3. $\begin{array}{r} 14.36 \\ +\ 7.21 \\ \hline \end{array}$
4. $\begin{array}{r} 8.63 \\ +\ 5.78 \\ \hline \end{array}$
5. $\begin{array}{r} 32.27 \\ +\ 12.21 \\ \hline \end{array}$

Round up. Then estimate the difference.

6. $\begin{array}{r} 6.7 \\ -\ 2.6 \\ \hline \end{array}$
7. $\begin{array}{r} 32.5 \\ -\ 16.3 \\ \hline \end{array}$
8. $\begin{array}{r} 99.95 \\ -\ 46.43 \\ \hline \end{array}$
9. $\begin{array}{r} 6.42 \\ -\ 2.46 \\ \hline \end{array}$
10. $\begin{array}{r} 16.8 \\ -\ 10.6 \\ \hline \end{array}$

Use rounding to estimate each sum or difference. Then write whether the actual sum or difference is **over** or **under** the reference point 20.

11. $11.36 + 9.27$

12. $6.2 + 18.8$

13. $33.7 - 9.6$

_____ _____ _____

Using Critical Thinking

Flow charts show a step-by-step way of doing things.
Different shapes are used for the different steps.

Start. or Stop. Instruction Question

Use the flowchart to answer these
questions.

1. What is the first step?

_____

2. What is the question in the flow
chart?

_____

3. If the word is even, what do you do
next?

_____

4. What is the sum of the word DOG?

_____

5. Is the word DOG even or odd?

_____

6. The word is DUCK. Is this word
even?

_____ What is the next step?

_____

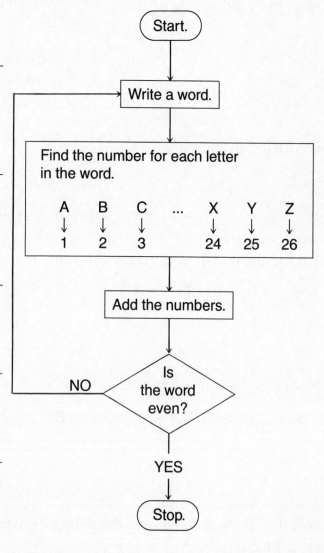

Start.

Write a word.

Find the number for each letter
in the word.

A   B   C   ...   X   Y   Z
↓   ↓   ↓   ↓   ↓   ↓
1   2   3   24   25   26

Add the numbers.

Is
the word
even?

NO

YES

Stop.

Special Quotients

How many wrappers are needed to put 120 coins into rolls of 40 coins each?

{120}   {40}

12 tens ÷ **4** tens = **3**

120 ÷ **40** = **3**

        or

$$\begin{array}{r} 3 \\ 40\overline{)120} \\ -\underline{120} \\ 0 \end{array}$$

$$\begin{array}{r} 3 \\ \textbf{4 tens}\overline{)\textbf{12 tens}} \end{array}$$

Divide.

1. $30\overline{)240}$ (3 tens)24 tens   **2.** $50\overline{)350}$ (5 tens)35 tens   **3.** $80\overline{)560}$ (8 tens)56 tens

4. $80\overline{)240}$ **5.** $70\overline{)560}$ **6.** $90\overline{)450}$ **7.** $70\overline{)420}$ **8.** $20\overline{)180}$

9. $10\overline{)80}$ **10.** $30\overline{)120}$ **11.** $60\overline{)480}$ **12.** $40\overline{)360}$ **13.** $80\overline{)720}$

14. $70\overline{)630}$ **15.** $20\overline{)120}$ **16.** $90\overline{)720}$ **17.** $60\overline{)420}$ **18.** $80\overline{)640}$

Rewrite these problems. Then divide.

19. $120 ÷ 40$ **20.** $480 ÷ 80$ **21.** $180 ÷ 90$

$40\overline{)120}$

Dividing by Tens: 1-Digit Quotients

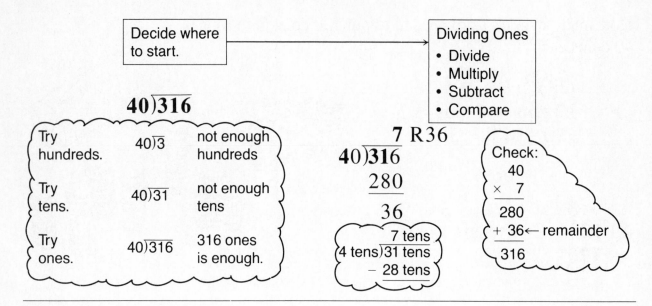

Decide where to start.

40)316

Try hundreds.	40)3	not enough hundreds
Try tens.	40)31	not enough tens
Try ones.	40)316	316 ones is enough.

Dividing Ones
• Divide
• Multiply
• Subtract
• Compare

$$\begin{array}{r} 7 \text{ R}36 \\ 40\overline{)316} \\ 280 \\ \hline 36 \end{array}$$

7 tens
4 tens)31 tens
− 28 tens

Check:
$$\begin{array}{r} 40 \\ \times\ 7 \\ \hline 280 \\ +\ 36 \leftarrow \text{remainder} \\ \hline 316 \end{array}$$

Divide and check.

1. 30)286   Check

3 tens)28 tens
− 27 tens

30
× 9
270

2. 50)237   Check

5 tens)23 tens
− 20 tens

3. 30)223   Check

4. 50)473   Check

5. 70)565   Check

Rewrite these problems. Then divide and check.

6. 293 ÷ 40   Check   **7.** 327 ÷ 60   **8.** 256 ÷ 30

40)293

Dividing: 1-Digit Quotients

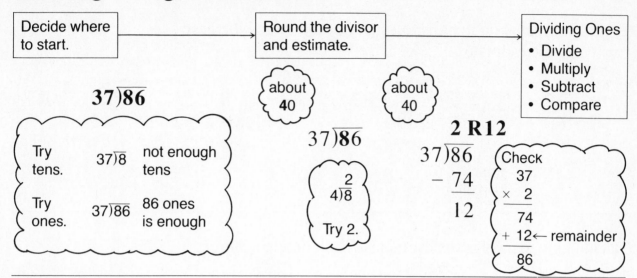

Decide where to start.	→	Round the divisor and estimate.	→	Dividing Ones
				• Divide
				• Multiply
				• Subtract
				• Compare

37)86

about 40   about 40

Try tens. 37)8 not enough tens

Try ones. 37)86 86 ones is enough

37)86

2
4)8

Try 2.

2 R12
37)86
− 74
12

Check
  37
× 2
  74
+ 12 ← remainder
  86

Divide and check.

about 20

1. 21)67   3 R   Check
         ---63   21
          4   2)6   3   ×_____

remainder → + _____

about 30

2. 28)67   2   Check
                    28
              3)6   2   ×_____

about?

3. 19)45   Check
                    2)4   2   ×_____

Check

4. 12)49

Check

5. 38)47

Check

6. 23)95

Rewrite these problems. Then divide and check.

7. 70 ÷ 31   Check   **8.** 50 ÷ 24   **9.** 82 ÷ 39

31)70

Changing Estimates

If your estimated quotient is too small or too large, you have
to change the estimate.

(30)

$$\begin{array}{r} 2 \\ 26\overline{)80} \\ -52 \\ \hline 28 \end{array}$$ ← greater than 26

(2 is too **small**. Try 3.)

$$\begin{array}{r} 3 \text{ R2} \\ 26\overline{)80} \\ -78 \\ \hline 2 \end{array}$$

(10)

$$\begin{array}{r} 8 \\ 11\overline{)80} \\ -88 \\ \hline \end{array}$$ ← too large

(8 is too **large**. Try 7.)

$$\begin{array}{r} 7 \text{ R3} \\ 11\overline{)80} \\ -77 \\ \hline 3 \end{array}$$

Decide how to change the estimates. Then divide again.

(20)

1. $$\begin{array}{r} 3 \\ 16\overline{)68} \\ -48 \\ \hline 20 \end{array}$$ ← greater than 16

(3 is too small. Try 4.)

$$\begin{array}{r} 4 \text{ R} \\ 16\overline{)68} \\ -64 \\ \hline 4 \end{array}$$

(10)

2. $$\begin{array}{r} 5 \\ 12\overline{)53} \\ -60 \\ \hline \end{array}$$ ← too large

(5 is too large. Try 4.)

$$\begin{array}{r} 4 \\ 12\overline{)53} \end{array}$$

(Finish dividing.)

(20)

3. $$\begin{array}{r} 2 \\ 17\overline{)54} \\ -34 \\ \hline 20 \end{array}$$ $17\overline{)54}$

(40)

4. $$\begin{array}{r} 1 \\ 37\overline{)78} \\ -37 \\ \hline 41 \end{array}$$ $37\overline{)78}$

(10)

5. $$\begin{array}{r} 2 \\ 13\overline{)25} \\ -26 \end{array}$$ $13\overline{)25}$

6. $$\begin{array}{r} 2 \\ 23\overline{)45} \\ -46 \end{array}$$ $23\overline{)45}$

7. $$\begin{array}{r} 2 \\ 28\overline{)89} \\ -56 \\ \hline 33 \end{array}$$ $28\overline{)89}$

8. $$\begin{array}{r} 3 \\ 31\overline{)90} \\ -93 \end{array}$$ $31\overline{)90}$

Divide. Change your estimates if necessary.

9. $17\overline{)70}$

10. $12\overline{)60}$

11. $23\overline{)50}$

Name _____

Mixed Practice

Many strategies can be used to solve problems.
Here is a list of strategies.

Act It Out	Guess and Check
Use Objects	Make a Table
Choose an Operation	Look for a Pattern
Draw a Picture	Use Logical Reasoning
Make an Organized List	Work Backward

Example: Theo is taller than Pedro. Dave is shorter than
Pedro. Kirk is taller than Theo. Who is the tallest?

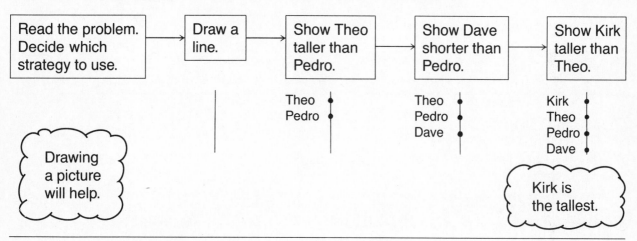

Choose a strategy from the list to solve each problem.

1. Sierra bought 8 records. Each
record cost $6. Then she spent $5
for a tape. How much money did
Sierra start with if she had $2 left?

_____

2. Arif has saved $14. He bought a
book for $5. Then he earned $8
baby-sitting. How much money
does he have now?

_____

3. The teacher asked for 1 boy and 1
girl to help him. 3 boys and 2 girls
wanted to help. How many ways
could the teacher choose?

_____

4. There were 3 beans in the first
bag, 6 beans in the second bag, 9
beans in the third bag, and so on.
How many beans were in the sixth
bag?

_____

Name _____

Dividing by Tens: 2-Digit Quotients

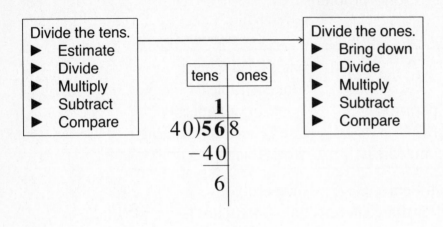

Divide the tens.
▶ Estimate
▶ Divide
▶ Multiply
▶ Subtract
▶ Compare

Divide the ones.
▶ Bring down
▶ Divide
▶ Multiply
▶ Subtract
▶ Compare

tens	ones
1	

40)56 8
−40
  6

tens	ones
1 4	R8

40)56 8
−40 ↓
16 8
−16 0
    8

Check:
  40
× 14
160
 40
560
+ 8
568

Divide and check.

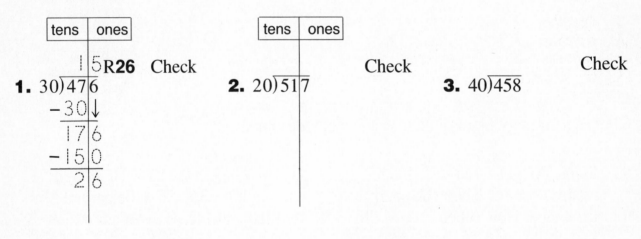

tens	ones
1 5	R26

1. 30)47 6
−30 ↓
17 6
−15 0
 2 6
    Check

tens	ones

2. 20)51 7
    Check

3. 40)458
    Check

4. 50)613
    Check

5. 30)900
    Check

6. 10)854
    Check

Dividing: 2-Digit Quotients

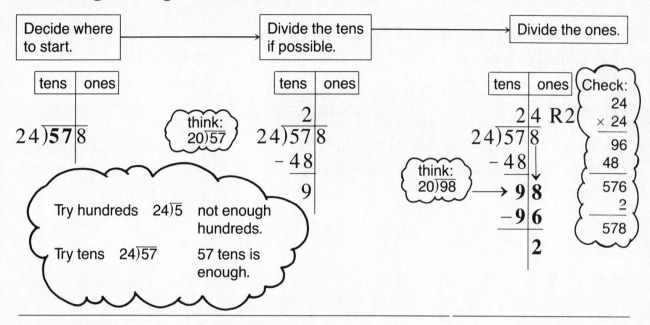

| Decide where to start. | → | Divide the tens if possible. | → | Divide the ones. |

tens | ones

24)57|8

think: 20)57

Try hundreds 24)5 not enough hundreds.

Try tens 24)57 57 tens is enough.

tens | ones

2
24)57|8
−48
9

tens | ones

24 R2
24)57|8
−48
→ 9|8
−9|6
2

think: 20)98

Check:
24
× 24
96
48
576
2
578

Find the quotients. Check your answers.

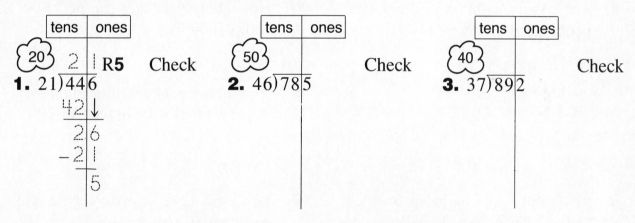

tens | ones

20 2 | R5   Check
1. 21)44|6
42↓
2|6
−2|1
5

tens | ones

50   Check
2. 46)78|5

tens | ones

40   Check
3. 37)89|2

Check
4. 29)788

Check
5. 34)538

Check
6. 65)671

Using a Calculator

For some division problems, a calculator shows the quotient as a decimal number. You need to interpret it to solve the problems.

Jane bought 1,250 apples. A bag holds 34 apples.

Questions:

▶ How many bags can Jane completely fill?

▶ How many bags does Jane need to carry all 1,250 apples?

  1,250 ÷ 34

Answers:

Jane can completely fill 36 bags.

Jane needs 37 bags.

Use a calculator to help solve these problems. Remember to interpret the decimal quotient.

1. The cook bought 543 rolls. Each package holds 1 dozen rolls.

▶ How many packages can he completely fill?

_____

▶ How many packages does he need to get all 543 rolls in packages?

_____

2. There are 1,247 balloons for the festival. Each hour 24 balloons are let go. How many hours will it take before all the balloons are let go?

_____

3. Leno has 1,420 words to type. He can type 36 words a minute. Will he be finished in 9 minutes?

_____

4. There are 265 campers signed up for volleyball teams. Each team needs 15 players. How many complete teams can be formed?

_____

5. Juice comes in packages of 16 bottles. 154 people have to be served. How many packages of juice are needed?

_____